*B*usiness Matters:

A GUIDE FOR SPEECH-LANGUAGE PATHOLOGISTS

Lee Ann C. Golper
Janet E. Brown
Editors

AMERICAN
SPEECH-LANGUAGE-
HEARING
ASSOCIATION

The **American Speech-Language-Hearing Association** (ASHA) is the national professional, scientific, and credentialing association for audiologists, speech-language pathologists, and speech, language, and hearing scientists. **ASHA** works to promote the interests of these professionals and to advocate for people with communication disabilities.

Table of Contents

Foreword

I am very pleased to have the opportunity to introduce this book to members of the speech-language pathology (SLP) profession. Over the past ten years, there has been significant interest in the area of business practices in speech-language pathology. This interest in the "business of our profession" is likely the result of many factors—increased sophistication among practitioners, increased profitability and productivity demands from employers, growth in private practice, and a host of other real world issues.

Three years ago when I had the pleasure of serving as ASHA's vice president of professional practices in SLP, I asked Lee Ann Golper to chair a committee that would study the needs of ASHA members regarding the business aspects of our profession and, to the degree possible, to develop resources to support this interest. Under Dr. Golper's expert guidance, a committee of dynamic leaders, Evie Hagerman, Pete Johnson, Ann Kummer, Pat Rogers, and John Torrens, from a variety of work settings, generated a host of documents and resources to support SLPs in all aspects of practice management. This book represents the product of this enthusiastic volunteer committee. I am both impressed with and grateful for the work of these colleagues, all leaders with expertise in various aspects of business practice in speech-language pathology.

My hope is that every ASHA member with management or leadership responsibilities will take time to examine this book and will find information that benefits their practice, informs their decision making, and allows them to serve people with communication disorders with utmost efficiency and quality. I believe that experienced professionals, individuals who aspire to leadership positions, and students in graduate programs will all find this book to be an important addition to their professional library.

Alex F. Johnson, PhD

2005 President-Elect, ASHA; 2000-2002 Vice President for Professional Practices in Speech-Language Pathology; Professor and Chair, Department of Audiology and Speech- Language Pathology, Wayne State University.

About the Authors

This book was a team effort. The contributing authors include those of us who served on the ASHA Ad Hoc Committee on Business Practices in Speech-Language Pathology: Lee Ann Golper, (chair) Evie Hagerman, Pete Johnson, Ann Kummer, Pat Rogers, John Torrens, and Janet Brown, ex officio. **Business Matters** is an extension of the committee's activities. Lee Ann Golper and Janet Brown served as the co-editors of the text. All authors partnered with one another to write, review, and edit drafts of the individual chapters and collectively brought decades of business practices and management experience in a wide range of service areas to the final product.

Lee Ann C. Golper, PhD, CCC-SLP

Lee Ann Golper is an Associate Professor in the Department of Hearing and Speech Sciences, Vanderbilt University School of Medicine. Her clinical and teaching interests include neurologic communication disorders and gerontology. She is the author of a textbook on medical speech-language pathology, and she lectures and consults on topics related to health services administration. Dr. Golper is the Administrative Director of Clinical Programs in Speech-Language Pathology, Vanderbilt Bill Wilkerson Center.

Lee Ann C. Golper

Janet E. Brown, MA, CCC-SLP

Janet Brown is the Director of Health Care Services in SLP at ASHA. Before coming to ASHA, Ms. Brown held various positions as a researcher, clinician, and clinical supervisor in acute care and rehabilitation hospitals, as well as in home health, outpatient, and long term care. At ASHA, Ms. Brown facilitates the development of resources for SLPs working in health care settings.

Janet E. Brown

Evie Hagerman, MS, CCC-SLP

Evie Hagerman is an Assistant Professor, Baker University School of Professional and Graduate Studies, School of Business and Management, with faculty leadership and teaching responsibilities. Ms. Hagerman has over 25 years of experience as Director of Speech Pathology, Audiology and Hearing Conservation for the 14 hospitals of Health Midwest. She is an assistant professor of business and management at The Baker University School of Professional and Graduate Studies.

Evie Hagerman

Peter Johnson

Ann Kummer

Patricia Rogers

John Torrens

Peter Johnson, PhD, CCC-SLP

Pete Johnson has an Executive Graduate Degree in Health Care Financial Management in addition to his graduate degrees in speech-language pathology. Dr. Johnson is the Speech Mentor with Select Medical Rehabilitation Services and a Clinical and Research Affiliate with the University of South Florida. He works with SLPs to develop clinical practice patterns. He is also the co-chair of the FLASHA Reimbursement Committee and is STAR (State Advocate for Reimbursement) representative to ASHA for reimbursement.

Ann Kummer, PhD, CCC-SLP

Ann Kummer is the Director of Speech Pathology at Cincinnati Children's Hospital Medical Center. This program is one of the largest and most respected speech-language pathology programs in the country with eight locations in the greater Cincinnati area. Dr. Kummer is Professor of Clinical Pediatrics at the University of Cincinnati Medical Center and the author of many professional articles, book chapters, and a textbook on cleft palate and craniofacial anomalies.

Patricia Rogers, MA, CCC-SLP

Pat Rogers is the Executive Vice President and Director of the Therapy Division of The Chesapeake Center, Inc. She founded Chesapeake with her husband Robert P. Rogers, MBA, in 1986. Chesapeake has two divisions. The therapy services division provides pediatric speech-language, occupational, and physical therapy as well as education services; and the medical services division provides medical personnel to the Department of Defense. Chesapeake has 200 employees.

John Torrens, PhD, CCC-SLP

John Torrens is the President and Executive Director of InterActive Therapy Group. He started the company as a solo practice in 1995 and now has over 150 employees with offices throughout New York State. Dr. Torrens earned a PhD in Business Administration from Northcentral University in addition to his masters in SLP from Syracuse University. His clinical work is in early intervention, and his academic interests include telepractice utilization and practice management.

Acknowledgments

The authors gratefully acknowledge the expert content reviews provided by ASHA staff members Mike Guerrieri, Mark Kander, Ingrid Lusis, Janet McNichol, Doug Plesh, Jim Potter, Paula Starr, and Steve White. ASHA members Phil Loverso, Wren Newman, Paul Rao, and Nancy Swigert also provided invaluable critiques, reviews, and comments on the manuscript, which have been incorporated into the final product. Alex Johnson, who was kind enough to provide us with the Foreword for this book, initially brought all of us together to form an ad hoc committee charged with addressing a membership need to better understand business practices. With ongoing inspiration from Alex, the committee not only completed this book but also produced two ASHA practice policy documents on knowledge and skills in business practices for speech-language pathologists.

The final production of this book is the work of Michele Newman, who provided copyediting and overall coordination, and Tarja Carter, who designed the graphics. Donna Vernon provided the desktop expertise. Special thanks to Joanne Jessen, ASHA's Publications Director, and Rick Henderson, Marketing and Sales Director, for seeing an opportunity to take ASHA publications in a new direction.

Finally, each of us wants to express our thanks to our spouses and family members (Tom, Rick, Joanne, John, Dennis, Bob, Lisa, and Deanna) who provided their support to us in this and in so many of our professional endeavors through the years.

Introduction

Business Matters: A Guide for Speech-Language Pathologists was prepared with many different readers in mind: students, clinical fellows, clinicians in practice, private practice owners, managers and organizational leaders, academic and clinical educators—individuals who have firsthand knowledge about the business side of clinical services in speech-language pathology (SLP) as well as those who haven't thought much about it. The information we review here is organized by topic areas rather than by settings. The contributing authors are program directors and leaders who come from a variety of work settings, both medical and nonmedical, and who provide services to clients throughout the life span. Although this book has most direct application to the various types of health service settings (hospitals, home health, skilled nursing facilities, university clinics, inpatient rehabilitation facilities, and outpatient clinics), much of the subject matter also applies to nonmedical settings such as private and public schools, preschools, and early intervention programs. This book is not a "how to" guide for starting a private practice, but all of the topics are equally relevant to private practitioners.

The title of the book, ***Business Matters***, captures not only the content of the book—the *matters* of our professional business—but also reinforces the message that business indeed *matters*. One of our goals is to emphasize the notion that business practices are highly important concerns for all of us. In the United States at least, knowing something about the business of health care is essential to our effectiveness as clinicians. Historically, speech-language pathologists have kept business considerations at a distance for fear of being ethically compromised; in today's environment, closing your eyes to the connection between service delivery and the business components that support it puts your clients and your organization at risk. From a personal standpoint, it also affects your value to your employer and your potential for career advancement. ASHA's publication of this book underscores the general recognition of the need for this information in our profession.

We were especially interested in providing a book that would prepare entry level clinicians for their journey into the workforce. We wouldn't plan a trip to a foreign country without finding out ahead of time a few things about the culture, language, and landscape. One of the intents of this book is to introduce some of the language and describe the landscape. This book is also intended as a guide for practicing clinicians and those of us in management and leadership positions. One goal is to provide quality benchmarks for clinicians, managers, and leaders to judge the merits of the organization where they are working with regard to its service delivery, human resources, business ethics, and care practices.

For our academic and clinical educator colleagues, **Business Matters** is intended to provide a context for clinical training to better match preparation with practice. We make no apologies for the use of business and management jargon throughout the book. We use words like *vision*, *process*, *workflow*, and *bottom line* because they are just part of the vocabulary of the business world. Ultimately, the goal is to enhance the success of our graduates as they enter the workforce and to help them find satisfying careers. We feel it is important for graduates to be well aware of the expectations of the community they are about to join. Those of us who chose academic careers were prepared during our doctoral studies to navigate the world of promotion, tenure, professional service, grant writing, accreditation processes, institutional review boards, and the like. Similarly, those of us entering clinical careers should be prepared to navigate the world of productivity, preauthorizations, insurance documentation, compliance rules, and privacy protections.

To canvas relevant topics and take into account different practice settings in SLP, we have prepared nine chapters. Wherever useful to illustrate a point, case studies are provided, either embedded within chapters or in a separate section at the end of the book when the example relates to more than one chapter. Chapters are also supplemented by resource lists, "tips," and examples of forms and letters. The information provided in the Appendices may be copied and adapted without permission.

We begin with Leadership (Chapter 1). Leadership is the means by which organizations accomplish the goals and conduct the programmatic activities that are reviewed in this book. It seemed fitting to define some of the key characteristics of leadership and how each of us, regardless of job title, has opportunities for leadership in our work as speech-language pathologists. Next, we look at Service Delivery (Chapter 2). Service delivery is the scaffold upon which our clinical work is supported. To understand service delivery, we look at everything from why productivity is an issue for all of us to the importance of ethics in business practices. Following that, we cover the basic language and the nuts and bolts of Financial Management (Chapter 3). We look at examples of accounting procedures and defining practices and concepts that are applied in clinical financial management. For many of us, the world of financial management can seem like "WTMI" (way too much information); however, it is important to remember that at the heart of business practices, and any other budget-based activity, is the *bottom line*—the profit and loss statement comparing revenues and expenses. Just knowing how to read and interpret a financial statement is a useful skill to have regardless of where we work.

In the next chapter, we take a look at what we broadly call Standards and Compliance (Chapter 4). In that chapter, we review the source of many of the rules and regulations that we encounter in a health care setting and, more importantly, the reasons behind them. We stress the importance of standards in service delivery to reduce risk and, thus, save costs. Without understanding why regulations, standards, policies, and procedures exist, clinicians might tend to view them as arbitrary rather than necessary protections. Complying with standards ensures that any risks to the organization, both legal and financial, are minimal. And, compliance is never optional.

After acknowledging that rules and standards are an integral part of health services delivery, we then review the topic of Quality and Performance Improvement (Chapter 5). It is here we make the point that compliance with standards alone will not ensure the provision of *quality* services. Quality is ephemeral; it is defined from multiple perspectives and is a constantly changing target. It is a perception, an attitude. Maintaining quality requires a commitment to performance improvement. We define what a PI program is, and how different groups (leaders, managers, clinicians) work together to ensure quality is maintained. Next, as if anyone needed to be reminded, we remind you that Technology (Chapter 6) helps organizations to maintain efficiencies. In business settings, these efficiencies usually translate to cost savings. Technology, used appropriately, can be an important investment and can serve to eliminate or reduce time consuming activities.

The next chapter, Personnel Management, delves into the topic of managing human resources effectively. In a people-oriented business like speech-language pathology, well-trained and committed clinicians are our most valuable commodity. When you consider that the expenses for most SLP departments are predominantly salaries and fringe benefits, and the cost of turnover in any organization can be substantial, it seems obvious that competent, qualified, and satisfied employees are absolutely essential to the financial success of a program.

In the final two chapters we look at Marketing (Chapter 8) and Advocacy (Chapter 9). The Marketing chapter provides a comprehensive review of marketing as an important business strategy and practice. We discuss many of the key activities and considerations that go into promoting speech-language pathology services within a competitive marketplace. Following this discussion of the essentials of marketing, we discuss activities and strategies involved in advocacy. Advocacy can involve promoting ourselves, our program, our profession, and the interests of our clients. Advocacy involves persuading decision makers to make decisions in our favor. Decision makers include supervisors, administrators, or others who direct policies within our own organization as well as policy makers in larger spheres, such as legislative bodies, insurance companies, or coalitions of organizations. Advocacy stresses working from our strengths, both individually and in groups, to obtain desired outcomes for our clients and our profession and for our own interests.

We enjoyed putting this book together. As the "About the Authors" statement and the Acknowledgments section attest, this was truly a team effort. The information in this book draws from a deep well of management and business practice experience within an outstanding group of contributing authors, along with advice, editing, and input from selected peer reviewers, and subject matter experts within the ASHA staff. The overriding motivation for this book was simply to benefit the members of the American Speech-Language-Hearing Association by providing information that is not otherwise available for them and that can take years of "on-the job" experience to acquire. The authors hope to help speech-language pathologists manage some of the challenges that come with practicing in a health service delivery setting today and to prevent confusion, frustration, and burnout by providing conceptual knowledge, tools, and technical advice in the *business matters* of our profession.

Lee Ann C. Golper and Janet E. Brown
Editors

Chapter 1
Leadership

Leaders and managers in speech-language pathology (SLP) service delivery settings face a number of challenges. They need to protect the financial welfare of the organization in the face of declining reimbursement. They are expected to contain costs despite rising expenses. They must seek service delivery efficiencies while contending with mounting documentation and regulatory expectations. They strive to ensure quality of care to individuals with communicative impairments while keeping employees both productive and satisfied and competing with other providers in the marketplace.

Chapter Focus

Leadership provides the means for achieving all of the organizational goals that are discussed in this text. In this chapter, we begin by looking at the differences between a leader and a manager, and then we consider the importance of the **organizational mission**, **vision**, **values**, and **strategic planning**. We will also discuss **sources of power** available to leaders, **leadership activities** and **leadership styles**, and **characteristics of effective leadership**.

What is a Leader?

A leader is a person who guides and directs other people toward an objective. An effective leader earns the trust and the loyalty of others and influences others to follow a certain path. Leadership involves directing others toward the achievement of goals.

Leadership is a partnership; it asks the follower to accept direction and the leader to give it. How the leader influences others to follow direction can vary, but ultimately, this influence depends upon a balanced relationship between a leader and the followers in a group. We often think of leaders as those who are in positions of authority. Leadership does not necessarily require any special authority.

Learning Outcomes

Describe the differences in focus and actions between a leader and a manager.

Discuss the roles and responsibilities of a leader.

Describe the sources of power that a leader may use to influence others.

Identify different leadership styles.

List various attributes of effective leaders.

We can all think of people in authority who are not very effective leaders. On the other hand, Mohandas Gandhi had no formal authority but was a gifted leader (Heifetz, 1995). Leadership is situation-specific. Anyone can be a leader if the circumstances demand it and if they use the skills, resources, and sources of power that are required.

In a clinical setting, it is important for all staff members to understand that even if they do not hold a position of authority, they will frequently be expected to serve and behave as a leader. For example, staff speech-language pathologists may be asked to act as leaders of their clients' treatment "teams," which include the client, family members, and other professionals.

What is a Manager?

A manager is someone who oversees the day-to-day operations of an organization. A manager implements the management plans that were developed by the leader.

Although the roles of leader and manager are not mutually exclusive, our personalities may cause us to prefer one role over the other. One author observes that managers are individuals who "enjoy process" and "seek stability and control" while leaders are individuals who "tolerate chaos and lack of structure" (Zaleznik, 2004, p.74). Heifetz (1995) uses the analogy of dancers on a dance floor. Managers are those who are engaged in the dance on the dance floor while leaders are required to have a view from the balcony. Leaders are expected to discern the direction and movements of all the dancers and to know "who is dancing with whom and in what patterns" (p. 253).

Difference between a Manager and a Leader

Leader	Manager
Originates ideas	Follows directions
Asks what and why	Asks how and when
Has global perspective	Has a day-to-day perspective
Looks toward the future	Focuses on the present
Watches the horizon	Watches the bottom line
Develops	Implements
Makes the rules	Plays the game
Promotes change	Maintains a steady course
Plans	Does
Takes initiative and risks	Follows a predetermined course
Deals with people	Deals with things
Looks at the forest	**Looks at the trees**

Leadership Roles

Leadership roles may fall into two related categories: the **visionary** role and the **motivational** role (Shortell & Kaluzny, 1994). As a visionary, the leader defines the mission, vision, values, and strategies of the organization or work group. These formal statements are especially important in an organization, but the notions are not very different from what is required for planning any life activity. Table 1-1 illustrates how a clinician might define his or her own mission, vision, values, and work strategy for his or her own job. Once the conceptual planning is complete, the leader must be able to translate the mission, vision, values, and strategies into action. This involves the motivational role: energizing, facilitating, and empowering others to accomplish the tasks.

Table 1-1.
Establishing a personal mission, vision, values, and strategy for your clinical work

Mission: To provide clinical SLP services to children who demonstrate communication disorders in a hospital setting.

Vision: To far surpass expectations in all service outcomes by providing timely, expert, evidence-based, culturally sensitive clinical services to all clients and their families.

Values: To conduct family-centered therapy with empathy, honesty, and professional integrity and to treat others with sensitivity and respect for cultural and linguistic diversity.

Strategy: To achieve my vision, I will–

- engage in ongoing continuing education to learn as much as possible about the current research related to the conditions I treat.
- strive continually to achieve and improve efficiencies in my services.
- get to know each individual client and his/her family to understand their concerns and goals.
- develop comprehensive, individualized treatment plans that are based on the goals and expectations of the client and family.
- communicate with staff in a timely manner.
- seek advice and feedback from others continually.
- ensure families are completely satisfied with my services.

Visionary Role

The visionary role encompasses the way in which leaders define, envision, strategize, and plan a path for others to follow. This is all done for the purpose of accomplishing certain goals through cooperation. Typically, leaders are in positions where they might develop the vision of an organization, while others may translate or articulate a pre-established vision of the organization. The success of an organization depends on leaders and managers developing and implementing their mission, vision, values, and strategic plans. For more on visionary leadership, see Chapter 5, Quality and Performance Improvement.

Mission: What is it we actually do?

An organization's mission is simply a formal statement of its primary purpose, activity, or function. For example, the mission of a school is *to educate children*. The mission of a children's hospital is *to treat sick children*. If the hospital is also a teaching, training, and research facility, part of its mission would also be *to engage in research and education*. Most organizations develop a mission statement that encompasses the essential functions of the organization. The mission statement serves both as a reminder of what the organization is in the business of doing and as a guideline for decision making. A proposed initiative for a new program, for example, would only be approved if the program were consistent with the mission of the organization.

Vision: Where are we going? Ideally, what do we want to be?

In contrast to an organization's mission, the organizational vision statement describes what the organization should look like in an ideal state. Vision statements contain lofty language and superlatives in an attempt to capture a model for the future. The vision serves as a destination, an idyllic goal for what the organization might, optimally, look like. Although having an organizational vision is important, there can be "visions" at all levels of an organization. It is important, however, that vision statements of individual units conform to and be consistent with the vision statement for the overall organization. For example, the vision of a university medical center may be *"We set the standard for excellence in family-centered medical services, cutting-edge research and science, and preparation of health professionals."* And the brain injury rehabilitation program at that facility may have a vision statement such as *"We are a national center of excellence in the provision of services to individuals with brain injury and their families, in the application of cutting-edge research and science in rehabilitation, and in the clinical education and training of team members."*

Typically, a vision statement takes into account all stakeholders. This would include **external customers** (e.g., clients, families, physicians, other professionals, and insurance companies), **internal customers** (e.g., senior management), and staff. Once determined, the vision is expressed as a written statement so that it clearly communicates the expectations of the leaders.

Values: What principles are important to us?

Values have to do with behavior and principles. Values are important to state explicitly for everyone in the organization, as they provide a behavioral expectation of performance and ensure everyone knows what is and is not acceptable. Value statements typically include language such as the following:

- We respect individuals, regardless of racial, cultural, or personal differences.
- We provide family-focused care.
- We treat others with dignity and compassion.

Developing a Strategy: How are we going to get there?

To ensure the organization meets its mission and strives continually to embody its vision, it is essential to develop a strategy or a roadmap for objectives and decision making. This strategy, or **strategic plan**, is a detailed action plan with defined responsibilities and timelines ultimately directed at realizing the vision of the leaders of the organization. When developing a strategic plan, the leaders consider what resources are required to meet their goals (money, people, time, materials, equipment, space, training, and technology). In addition, the leadership must consider the organization's "**S**trengths, **W**eaknesses, **O**pportunities, and **T**hreats" in achieving its goals—this systematic review is referred to as a **SWOT analysis**. Once defined, the strategic plan serves to focus employees and activities of the organization toward a common purpose.

Motivational Role and Sources of Power

Translating and articulating the mission, vision, values, and strategic plans of an organization brings to bear the leader's motivation role. The motivational role requires leaders to engage in training and coaching, energizing, empowering, and influencing others to accomplish the plans and goals of the organization. The success of these activities depends upon the leader's "power" or ability to influence others.

Although some may think that merely being the "boss" provides a source of authority that is sufficient to influence others, this is actually a misconception. A leader influences others through various means, and they are not always related to titles (e.g., "director").

There are many books and articles on leadership that discuss the leader's source of power to influence others. Although different labels are sometimes used, authors (Yukl, 1981; Hellriegel, Slocum & Woodman, 1983) have listed five basic sources of power in a work situation (Table 1-2).

Table 1-2.
Five Sources of Power

Legitimate (Position) Power	*I'm the boss, here is the plan.*
Reward Power	*If you go along with my plan, I will give you a raise, bonuses, time off, desirable assignments, more continuing education, recognition, etc.*
Coercive (Punishment) Power	*If you don't go along with my plan, I will take away your privileges, money, title, desirable work assignment, recognition, or job.*
Expert Power	*Trust me, I know what I'm talking about, and I know this is the best plan.*
Referent (Personal) Power	*Trust me, I care about you and your well-being and feel this is the best plan.*

Position power is the most obvious. The boss, by virtue of the position, is designated as a leader of the group with the authority to tell staff what to do, when to do it, and how to do it. The boss has the *right* to exert influence based on the expectations of this formal position. In a supervisory situation, the supervisor's power over the staff is based on the level of authority that is inherent in the position.

Related to position power is **reward power**. Reward power is the leader's ability to give the staff something of value in exchange for the work. Salary, benefits, and promotion are tangible types of reward. The reward or incentive does not need to be monetary to be effective, however. Recognition, respect, and special privileges or assignments can also be powerful sources of reward to influence others. In contrast, **punishment (coercive) power** is the ability to take something away. The employee may be coerced to comply with the wishes of the leader due to a fear of reprisal, loss of respect, embarrassment, loss of pay, less flexible work hours, or loss of job. Effective leaders use this form of power sparingly because it is likely to create resentment and negativity and erode personal power in the long run. Personal power has also been referred to as referent power. (Yukl, 1981; Hellriegel, Slocum & Woodman, 1983)

Expert power is not related to the leader's position. A leader is said to have expert power when employees or others recognize his or her special training, experience, knowledge, skill, or credentials as important to the success of the group. An effective leader must have sufficient experience and knowledge in appropriate areas to be perceived to have expert power. A leader with expert power engenders confidence. Experts are those who understand the issues and can take appropriate actions on behalf of the group. The leader's expertise makes employees feel that they are in good hands. The greater the expertise the leader has relative to the particular work setting or position, the more influence the individual will have. In speech-language pathology departments, leaders who have a clinical background may be more effective than those who have a business background because staff SLPs tend to think that other clinicians will better understand their work.

Finally, **personal power** refers to sources of influence that are tied to personality, for example, a leader's "charisma," communication skills, and other personal characteristics. This source of influence is directly linked to the "likeability" of the leader. How the leader treats others is the most important determinant for this type of power. Personal power doesn't come from a resume or a job title but is developed when the leader shows positive regard and respect for others, encourages others to achieve their best, and displays characteristics that engender trust, such as honesty and integrity. As a result of how they feel toward that individual, followers develop a strong personal identification with and loyalty to a leader with personal power.

Leaders with personal power tend to display what has been termed "emotional intelligence" (Goleman, 1995; 2004). Emotional intelligence is what business leaders refer to as "leading by feel" (Heifetz, 2004). Even though he acknowledges that emotional intelligence is critical for effective leadership, Heifetz points out that interpersonal skill, such as the ability to recognize the emotional makeup of others, may not be sufficient to gain authority or influence over others. Still, effective leaders need to possess the key qualities that are defined as part of emotional intelligence, such as self-awareness (the ability to understand one's own strengths and weaknesses), self-regulation, motivation, empathy, and social skills.

In the foregoing discussion of sources of power, the first three forms of power (position, reward, and punishment power) are typically endowed and associated with being the "boss." Nonetheless, there is general agreement (Yukl, 1981; Hellriegel, Slocum & Woodman, 1983) that expert and, especially, personal power are far more effective sources of influence. A person who has authority but lacks expert or personal power may find it difficult to exert effective influence over others.

The Leader-Follower Relationship

In addition to considering the sources of power available to him or her, the leader should understand the mutual dependency between leaders and followers. Both the parties need to get something in the bargain. In the work setting, the leader is dependent on the employee for a certain amount and quality of work. The employee in return is dependent on the leader for tangible and intangible rewards. These rewards may be material (salary) or psychological (recognition). There is an expectation between leaders and followers of reciprocity, balance, and equity in these exchanges or the relationship will not work. For example, if an employee feels that he/she is not adequately paid or recognized for work performed, he/she will probably look for another position.

If the leader feels that the organization is paying for more work than it is getting from the employee, the employee may be out of a job. An effective leader seeks to maintain a balance for employees between work expectations and compensations. Making sure the employee feels compensated and appreciated can make the difference between a harmonious working relationship and a contentious, resentful one.

With regard to the notion of balance in the relationship in the leader-follower relationship, the concept of the "boss" and "subordinate" should be examined. Contrary to the common perception, a subordinate does not work "for" the boss. Instead, both are employees working for each other. An effective boss might be better described as a "servant leader." If the employee is happy with the rewards and has all the necessary resources for the job, he or she is likely to provide quality services, be productive, and stay in the position. Since the cost of staff turnover can be significant, employee satisfaction is an important priority for the boss.

Leadership Activities and Responsibilities

Coaching

A coach is someone who improves the performance of others by training, mentoring, monitoring, encouraging, providing feedback, and holding others accountable. Why is coaching an important activity and responsibility for a leader? Leaders are always dependent on others to accomplish tasks toward the goals. Therefore, the leader must ensure that the others have the knowledge and skills to do the job well and efficiently.

Coaching includes ensuring that others receive the encouragement they need so that they have confidence and a positive attitude. In short, coaching ensures employees know they *can* do the job and *want* to do it well. It is important that employees feel competent and capable to do a job. The more knowledgeable and trained the employee is, the better the ultimate outcome will be. A successful leader takes pride in the development, success, and accomplishments of those under his or her leadership. The leader should foster a culture of continuous learning through coaching and mentoring at all levels in the organization. When coaching and continuous learning are part of the culture, the quality of the services delivered improves, and job satisfaction remains high.

Speech-language pathologists are generally adept at providing coaching in behavioral changes. Our profession naturally lends itself to teaching and helping others. These skills easily translate to coaching others (students, coworkers).

Assigning and Delegating Responsibility

An effective leader realizes that he or she must prioritize, assign, and delegate tasks. Good leaders determine what needs to be done and by whom. In fact, if the leader spends time on tasks that can, or should, be done by others, it leaves little time to attend to global or strategic matters. Assigning or delegating tasks is a form of time management for leaders, but it is also a way to help others develop skills and abilities and to take advantage of talents in the organization. Although tasks are often delegated through either assignment or delegation, there is a difference between the two.

Assigning refers to giving an employee highly detailed instructions on how to accomplish the task. This implies the need to monitor progress frequently, offer suggestions, and maintain control of the project at all times. Because many leaders want to be "in charge," the leader will often assign tasks but not give employees the freedom and authority to make independent or final decisions. Assignment is appropriate when an employee does not have adequate knowledge or skill to complete the task independently.

Delegating refers to defining the parameters of the final goal and then giving the person the responsibility, freedom, and authority to accomplish the goal as he or she sees fit. Delegation transfers authority and responsibility to another person to act for the leader. There are many advantages to delegating as compared to assigning tasks. In addition to freeing the leader from the burden of monitoring every step, delegating tasks develops a sense of responsibility, problem solving, and ownership of the activity by the employee. Taking personal responsibility for problem solving provides employees with an opportunity to understand the workings of the organization and ultimately, can result in a number of benefits to the organization: increased knowledge, skills, confidence, productivity, loyalty, and morale. In many cases, delegation to those who will be affected by the decisions can actually improve decision quality and acceptance. Because of the many potential advantages to delegation, the leader should seek opportunities to delegate and involve others whenever possible.

Motivating

Although rewards in the form of salary and benefits are a primary motivation for taking a job for most of us, salaries alone do not define our job satisfaction. It is the leader's responsibility to be sure that the employee has the resources necessary to do the job and to feel supported. Finally, effective leaders understand that recognition, praise, and expressions of appreciation for doing a good job are highly motivating to employees—especially those in professional positions, such as speech-language pathologists.

Communicating

As speech-language pathologists, we know a thing or two about communication. However, we often forget that effective communication is just as important in organizations as it is in personal relationships. An effective leader is one who recognizes the importance of good communication skills and communicates with employees frequently, honestly, and clearly. If a leader is not proactive in communicating with employees, employees will rely on rumors and the "grapevine." Rumor mills are generally inaccurate and can be a destructive form of communication, undermining the leader's effectiveness.

The leader should keep employees informed of anything that has the potential to affect the employee, the department or unit, or the organization. This includes communicating clear expectations of performance, organizational goals and strategies, and any impending changes (new leadership, new programs). It is important to be open and honest in reporting both good and bad news. Sharing information has a positive effect on engendering trust, job satisfaction, and performance. Withholding information can have a negative effect resulting in anxiety, insecurity, and distrust. To be an effective communicator, the leader often needs to place anticipated changes into a context for the employees, to engage in what is called "change management." (Kirkpatrick, 1985). Leaders should be knowledgeable about internal and external forces that have the potential to affect the organization in both a positive or negative manner and to help others adapt to changes. To do so, it is important both to have the facts and to communicate them.

The leader should also be visible, available, and approachable to answer questions. Communication has to occur frequently and to take many forms: direct, person-to-person discussions; presentations at a staff meeting; memos; e-mails; newsletters; conference calls; or posted announcements.

Leadership Styles

Leadership behaviors and styles have been described and presented in a number of ways. One way to analyze your own leadership style is to consider whether you use task-oriented or people-oriented approaches to problems and whether you exercise control in an autocratic manner or use a more participative approach (Tannenbaum & Schmidt, 1973). The amount of control that a leader maintains can be seen on a continuum from autocratic to participative.

Task-Oriented versus People-Oriented Leaders

The task-oriented leader clarifies the job requirements and gets people to focus on performance, production, and accomplishment of the tasks. On the other hand, the people-oriented leader attends to the needs of the employees to get the job done.

Autocratic versus Participatory Leadership

The **autocratic (directive, boss-centered) leader** retains the authority to make decisions without input from others. This type of leader maintains a high degree of control, gives little freedom to the employees, and typically informs employees of decisions after they are made. This leadership style is best with employees who need a great deal of assistance or direction.

> If a leader is not proactive in communicating with employees, employees will rely on rumors and the "grapevine." Rumor mills are generally inaccurate and can be a destructive form of communication, undermining the leader's effectiveness.

In contrast, the **participative (supportive, employee-centered) leader** gives a great deal of control and freedom to employees. This leader may empower others to make decisions or may seek input from others and then make decisions based on that input. This leadership style is generally most effective with employees who are self-motivated and have the knowledge and skills to do the job without a great deal of supervision. This type of leader seeks to build the skills and self-confidence of the employees.

The above behaviors and styles each have advantages and disadvantages. Any particular style can be effective in certain situations, depending on the type of tasks to be performed; the knowledge, skill, and motivation of the employees; and the relationship between the employees and the leader. Although some leaders naturally are more comfortable with a particular style, effective leaders are those who are able to use a combination of leadership styles to meet the needs of each particular situation.

Effective Leadership

There are many articles and studies that have looked at the characteristics of effective leaders. As we said at the outset, what makes an effective leader depends largely on the situation and circumstances. Leaders are individuals who will accomplish goals through varied and unique methods, so there is no single blueprint for effective leadership. However, there are some characteristics effective leaders tend to have in common.

Character. Effective leaders adhere to a personal code of ethics. They can admit mistakes and apologize. When they demonstrate ambition, it is more for the accomplishments of the organization than for themselves. They are fair to all and a role model of courteous behavior. They do not use power for any personal gain. They are genuine and candid, modest, inspirational, and respectful of others. They have self-awareness, self-regulation, and self-discipline. Effective leaders display humility, integrity, diplomacy, tact, and grace under fire.

Interpersonal Relationships. Effective leaders listen to others. They communicate effectively one-to-one and in groups. They demonstrate respect for the time of others and are concerned about the welfare of employees. They recognize, reward, and genuinely appreciate the contributions of others. Effective leaders develop, and communicate confidence in, the abilities of others. They work cooperatively, give frequent positive feedback, display a positive attitude, and are courteous. Effective leaders support and empower others and celebrate their successes.

Competence and Drive. Effective leaders demonstrate they have the knowledge and skills to get the job done. They are ambitious and goal oriented. They are assertive and decisive. They have initiative and strive for results. They are willing to take risks. They are visionaries as well as problem solvers. They are optimistic and see setbacks as opportunities to try again. They can tolerate confusion and stress. Effective leaders are motivated to make a difference and are committed and passionate about the mission and vision of their department and organization.

Leading a Group or Team

Leading a small group requires the same skills as leading a large organization. All of the same qualities that apply to effective and successful leadership (source of influence, power, style, and leadership characteristics) come to bear in any leadership situation. The effective leader will help to determine the purpose (mission) or goal of the group, clarify expectations to the members, and guide the group to accomplish its tasks. (See Appendix A, Example of Chair and Member Responsibilities and Appendix B, Tips for Leading Committees or Teams.)

Summary

Becoming effective leaders and managers requires skills that can be learned and practiced in many life situations, not just in the workplace. You don't need to be in a position of authority to be a leader. In fact, mere authority (position power) is not generally the most effective source of influence on others. Expert power, which implies a demonstrated competence and skill, is a more effective base of influence than position or the power to give rewards or punishments. In most leadership situations, the greatest source of influence comes from personal power, related to a number of personal characteristics of the individual, referred to as emotional intelligence (Goleman, 1995). Clinical training and experience creates a natural stage for speech-language pathologists to develop leadership and management skills, such as coaching, motivating, and communicating; and for clinicians to bring expert and personal power to leadership roles within their organization and profession.

References

Goleman, D. (2004). What makes a leader? The best of HBR: Inside the mind of a leader. *Harvard Business Review, 82(1)*, 82-91.

Goleman, D. (1995). *Emotional intelligence*. New York: Bantam Books.

Heifetz, R. A. (2004). Question authority. Voices: Leading by feel. *Harvard Business Review, 82(1)*, 27 -37.

Heifetz, R. A. (1995). *Leadership without easy answers*. Cambridge, MA: Harvard University Press.

Hellriegel, D., Slocum, Jr., J. W., & Woodman, R. W. (1983). *Organizational behavior* (3rd ed.). St. Paul, MN: West Publishing Company. (10th ed., 2003, Mason, OH: South Western/Thomson).

Kirkpatrick, D. L. (1985). *How to manage change effectively*. San Francisco: Jossey-Bass.

Shortell, S. M., & Kaluzny, A. D. (Eds.). (1994). *Health care management: Organization design and behavior* (3rd ed.). Albany, NY: Delmar Publications. (4th ed., 1999).

Tannenbaum, R., & Schmidt, W. H. (1973). How to choose a leadership pattern. *Harvard Business Review, 51(3)*.

Yukl, G. A. (1981). *Leadership in organizations*. Englewood Cliffs, NJ: Prentice Hall. (5th ed., 2002).

Zaleznik, A. (2004). Managers and leaders: Are they different? The best of HBR. Inside the mind of a leader. *Harvard Business Review, 82(1)*, 74-81.

Chapter 2
Service Delivery

Service delivery in today's health care environment requires speech-language pathologists (SLPs) to deliver the highest quality of clinical services in the most cost-effective manner. This climate may cause clinicians to feel they are being pulled in two directions, trying to meet the demands of the employer organization while providing quality care. This conflict can result in frustration and burnout. Optimally, good service delivery practices complement and support quality client care, rather than distract from it.

Chapter Focus

This chapter examines elements of service delivery—the business side of clinical services. Program managers must understand and communicate the reasons behind service delivery practices, but the speech-language pathologist has to implement those practices in client care without diminishing quality. To understand some of the issues in play when attempting to provide cost-effective, quality services, the following topics are reviewed: **operating margin, productivity, benchmarks, reimbursement, coding, documentation, resource utilization,** and **ethical practices**.

Learning Outcomes

Describe reimbursement methods for SLP services.

Document services consistent with payer requirements.

Maximize resources and improve efficiencies in the workplace.

Apply ethical standards of practice in service delivery.

SLP Departments as Profit Centers

SLP departments in health care settings are expected to be profit centers, that is, the income they generate should meet or exceed the costs for providing services, including direct (salaries) and indirect costs (overhead). Unlike some other departments or services, such as nursing or nutrition, your services are expected to provide an operating margin, or profit to the organization, even if they are part of a larger entity, such as a rehabilitation department. Figure 2-1 illustrates how the operating margin is calculated for the SLP unit in a medical center.

Figure 2-1.
Calculation of Operating Margin

Program Costs		
	Professional Salaries (3 full time staff)	$150,000
	Fringe benefits (health insurance, paid leave, 401K, etc.)	$35,000
	Overhead/support and maintenance costs (materials, tests, supplies, mileage, facility and office space continuing education, .25 time clerical support)	$25,000
	Program Operating Costs	$210,000
Program Revenue		
	Projected Gross Billings	$420,000
	Projected Collections @ 54%	$226,800
Program Operating Margin		$16,800

Operating Margins

Although a positive operating margin at the end of the fiscal year (as in the example above) might appear to be a profit for the organization, in actual practice, these funds are put toward unforeseen costs in other areas, such as capital equipment purchases, investments in new program development, and salary increases. Month-to-month, the SLP program's operating margins may be positive (in the black) or negative (in the red), due to poor collections (payment for services) or unforeseen costs (recruitment of additional staff). To achieve a consistently positive operating margin, the clinical staff will be expected to deliver services in sufficient volume to meet or exceed the program's operating costs.

Monthly costs (salaries, fringes, maintenance) are generally fixed, but payment for services to offset these costs may lag months behind their billing date. Many factors influence the percent of reimbursements that are actually collected from different payers. The amount collected may represent only a percent of what was billed, anywhere from 0 to 100% depending on the payer; most programs expect to receive at least 50% to 65% of billed charges.

Understanding Productivity Targets

Productivity refers to some measurement of the efficiency of a clinician, program, department, or organization in delivering products or services. In clinical settings, productivity is usually defined as the ratio of the time actually spent providing direct, face-to-face services with the client (billed time) to the total time the clinician is paid to work (worked time). To achieve a productivity target, the time scheduled for direct client care will be slightly higher than the expected billable time, to allow for no shows, illness, and cancellations.

Whether or not an administrator explicitly sets a productivity target for the staff, he or she must use some type of productivity calculation to project the programs' staffing and revenue. Organizations that are "not for profit" still must meet productivity targets. Organizational budgets are developed by examining productivity data trends to see how well the organization has successfully met its targets in the past and what projections can be made about the future (see Chapter 3, Financial Management for further discussion).

If you are a manager, you will be expected to set productivity targets for billable time that will yield a percent of reimbursement sufficient to cover the program's costs. In our example described earlier (see Figure 2-1), if the SLP program typically collects 54% of billed services, the department will generate an operating margin of $16,800. If the annual gross billings are $420,000 and the facility collects only about 45% of its gross billings, then the department will have a negative operating margin (loss). Bearing that in mind, it is important that we make the best use of our time and use good documentation and coding practices to ensure the best return on effort for highest possible collections. Much of the time-consuming clinical activities required to prepare for, record, and communicate about client care are not billable to a payer (e.g., time spent on insurance verification, scheduling, chart review, report writing, travel, team meetings, phone calls). To meet budget expectations, managers and clinicians must set and meet productivity targets and look for ways to reduce nonbillable activities as much as is practical. (See Appendix C, Tips for Efficient Use of Time.)

Examples of Productivity Targets

Fernando works full time in a hospital from 8:00 a.m. to 5:00 p.m. with an hour for lunch. His productivity target is 5 billable hours for 8 paid hours or 62.5%. To achieve an average billable time of slightly higher than 60%, Fernando would need to have 5.5 to 6 hours of scheduled direct patient care time each day, depending on the no-show rates.

Cindy is paid by the hour to provide coverage for other SLPs in a large pediatric practice. Since she is not a staff employee and has only minimal administrative duties in patient care, her productivity requirement is quite high—90%. Consequently, if she works 20 hours in a given week, she would be expected to provide 18 hours of direct, billable patient contact.

Kia works full time in an outpatient clinic. She has cases scheduled back to back from 9:00 a.m. to 4:00 p.m. each day, with a caseload of roughly 30 clients per week for 1 hour sessions. On average, she has 8 or 10 cancellations through the week. Her scheduled time is fairly high (75%), but her actual productive time is 20-22 hours in a 40-hour work week, or roughly 50%-55%. To meet her minimum productivity target, her supervisor is working with her to find solutions to reduce the number of cancellations. They have prepared an attendance contract for clients and assigned an aide to make reminder calls to clients about their appointments. They have set a goal of no more than three cancellations per week. They are also considering a new policy that requires payment for no-shows.

$$\frac{\text{Billed Time}}{\text{Worked Time}} = \text{Productivity}$$

There is a direct relationship between the productivity of an organization and its financial status. In health care settings, the typical measures of productivity are –

- number of visits completed,
- number of procedures completed,
- amount of gross billings generated from those visits or procedures,
- reimbursement, or cash collected, for the services,
- ratio of actual, billable time spent with clients to actual worked time.

Since the largest part of SLP program costs are salaries and benefits, productivity directly supports staffing and salaries. Ultimately, the reimbursement collected from the clinical effort determines the financial viability of a SLP program, which, in turn, influences the viability and growth of the program.

Productivity and Staffing

Even in situations where a clinician's actual time spent with a client is not billed directly to a health plan (such as Medicare-covered inpatient services or nursing home stays), administrators rely on productivity data to monitor the adequacy of their staffing. Most programs have a staffing plan in place to ensure they have the right number of qualified staff for the service demands (see also Chapter 7, Personnel Management).

Benchmarks

Productivity measures are also used to create or compare to benchmarks. Benchmarks are targeted outcomes, ways to examine the efficiency of an organization, and may include service delivery data, such as client satisfaction ratings or scheduling delays. Benchmarks allow an individual or organization to set specific performance targets (e.g., "90% client satisfaction on department surveys"). Efficiency calculations may be established by an organization or compared to other benchmarks from comparison groups. Productivity benchmarks are some measure of the amount of service provided (e.g., billed time, number of visits, number of procedures, dollars billed), within a certain time frame compared to the costs and worked hours required for

$$\frac{\text{Cost Per Unit of Service}}{\substack{\text{Productivity Indicator} \\ \text{(e.g., billed time)}}} = \text{Costs to Provide Service}$$

providing the service. Productivity benchmarks are often captured as a **cost per unit of service** by taking the total costs to support the service and dividing by a productivity indicator (e.g., total hours of direct care, total number of visits or procedures) in a given time frame.

Factors in Productivity Variability

According to the American Speech-Language-Hearing Association's 2002 *Health Care Survey*, 93% of respondents from pediatric hospital settings reported having productivity targets, compared to 23% for respondents in home health. Home health clinicians are expected to see a certain number of clients within an allotted day or week. Efficiency is still a factor in their service delivery, even though they may not have "billable time" productivity targets. The survey data (see Table 2.1) indicate that clinicians across work settings report a productivity target of roughly 60% to 70% of worked time, with higher targets in skilled nursing and rehabilitation facilities.

Productivity targets and how productivity is measured and tracked will vary somewhat by setting and other factors, including the following:

Client characteristics

- Medically fragile children or acutely ill clients may not be able to tolerate therapy for a scheduled session.

Cancellations

- Inclement weather
- Client illness
- Staff illness or vacation
- Unanticipated scheduling conflicts (e.g., other appointments, tests)

Work setting and logistics

- Acute care inpatients are not always available on a set schedule if other procedures are being performed.
- Services provided to multiple settings or in clients' homes require travel time between locations.

Scheduling barriers

- Outpatient pediatric clients may not be available in the mornings.
- The radiology department may only schedule outpatient swallow studies two mornings a week.

Nonbillable time requirements

- Documentation
- Mandatory training events
- Professional education
- E-mail correspondence
- Phone calls

- Team meetings
- Staff meetings
- Performance improvement projects
- Preparation sessions
- Travel
- Supervision assignments

Table 2.1.
Productivity Survey Data by Work Setting (ASHA Health Care Survey, 2002a)

Setting	Two Most Common Productivity Targets	Reported by % of Respondents
General Medical Hospital	70%–79%	45%
	60%–69%	23%
Rehabilitation Hospital	70%–79%	51%
	80%–89%	24%
Pediatric Hospital	60%–69%	44%
	70%–79%	28%
Skilled Nursing Facility	70%–79%	50%
	80%–89%	31%
Home Health Agency or Client Home	70%–79%	26%
	60%–69%	24%
Outpatient or Speech/ Hearing Clinic	70%–79%	41%
	60%–69%	24%

Understanding Reimbursement

Whether you work for an organization or in private practice, you must comply with the payment requirements of reimbursement systems for the clinical services you provide. Although these processes may sometimes appear arbitrary and illogical, they are nonetheless mandated by payers or by the compliance mandates of their organization (see Chapter 4, Standards and Compliance). Forms, formats, and processes for meeting the requirements of payers can vary from one organization to the next. You can bring your own creative problem solving and streamlining ideas to the process, once you understand the basic mechanisms of the major reimbursement systems. The major options for health services coverage, not including the Veterans Affairs Medical Centers are –

- **insurance**,
- **managed care**,
- **private pay**,
- **Medicare** (federally funded and regionally managed),
- **Medicaid** (federally funded and state managed),
- **contracts, service agreements, and other third-party payers, such as Worker's Compensation**.

Insurance

Commercial insurance coverage is increasingly "managed," even if it is provided by an entity that is not formally incorporated or designated as a managed care organization. Government and commercial insurance entities are usually referred to as "health plans" because many are not traditional insurance plans. Health plans provide coverage for specified health benefits to individuals and families who enroll and pay a monthly premium (usually through a cost-sharing arrangement with their employer). Nearly all health plans have restrictions to access, coverage limits, and other cost containment policies. The fees set for reimbursement by health plans are based on aggregate data for charges submitted by all providers in their database for a given CPT code. Policies typically require a physician's referral for the SLP services to be covered. A physician's referral may not necessarily support the "medical necessity" of the SLP service. Only certain conditions and procedures will be covered as medically necessary. Consequently, it is advisable to get the SLP evaluation and treatment preauthorized or to receive a predetermination from the payer to verify that services are medically necessary and that service coverage requirements have been met prior to providing the services.

Explanation of Benefits

When a bill is submitted, the beneficiary (client or family) will receive an "Explanation of Benefits," or EOB, indicating what will and will not be covered by the policy. Each health plan may offer a range of insurance plans, and each company's coverage policies and processes are unique. For facilities or practices to be paid for services they provide, they must comply with the following:

- **Coverage policies**. For example, if a policy explicitly states that treatment for stuttering is not covered, or if stuttering is not explicitly on the list of covered conditions, then the provider may not be authorized to bill the insurance company for treatment of that condition. Policy benefits that exclude developmental disabilities may make it difficult to obtain coverage for services to children with language or phonological disorders, especially those that are not clearly related to a recognized medical cause (specific disease or injury). In such cases, the client, or his or her family, will be expected to pay for the noncovered services privately.

- **Authorization requirements**. Authorization for services prior to the initiation of SLP services may be required by some health plans even when SLP is said to be a covered service. The authorization will specify any frequency or duration limits and whether the covered services must occur within a set number of days. It is important to specify the number of days authorized for coverage; for example, an authorization of "one month" of therapy can mean either a calendar month, 20 days within a certain time frame, or a total of 30 different therapy visit days. Seeking preauthorization may increase chances for broader coverage (scope and/or duration), whether or not the health plan requires preauthorization. Unfortunately, insurance companies sometimes preauthorize treatment with disclaimers, such as the following: "Verification and explanation of benefits is not a guarantee of payment." "All benefits are paid subject to claim review." "Explanation of benefits on this date of preauthorization may be subject to change by the date of service." In other words, preauthorization is essential but not a guarantee of payment.

- **Insurance verification or referral processes**. If the client's coverage expired or has changed, the insurance plan listed in the medical record may not be valid; therefore, the services will not be reimbursed. If the insurance company requires that a physician complete a referral form before SLP services may be provided, then services will not be reimbursed if there is no "physician's order," or certification, obtained and on record. The payer may require the full, original signature of the physician (not initials, verbal telephone orders, or an order signed by a nurse on behalf of the doctor). The order has to be dated, and the order may need to state the exact days or duration of treatment requested by the physician.

- **Documentation requirements**. Documentation can vary depending upon the payer. The insurance company may require a particular form or format for recording procedure or visit data and may request specific information be provided on the claim form. Increasingly, payers (like Medicare) only accept electronic billing. In such cases, the provider is asked to submit written documentation only if the claims office requires additional information to process the bill after the initial review. Even if paper copies of clinical documentation are not submitted with the billing claims, the medical or clinical record must contain verification of every service that was billed. The basic rule is "if you didn't write it down, you didn't do it." Failure to have adequate documentation of a visit may result in denial of payment and may require the facility to reimburse payments already made.

- **Co-payment**. Depending upon the coverage stipulations and whether or not the provider is within network (see Managed Care, below), most insurance companies require some co-payment at the time of service. Dollar amounts may vary, but compliance rules require facilities to collect co-payments at the time of service.

- **Primary and secondary coverage**. Many clients have both primary and secondary coverage. In these cases, the primary provider may need to be billed for the service. If coverage is denied, the secondary payer will be billed. This becomes complicated when there are inconsistencies in coverage policies between primary and secondary coverage (e.g., the primary coverage is private insurance, and the secondary coverage is the state disability program).

> ...verify requirements for patient eligibility, coverage, authorized visits, documentation, and limitations on treatment with the benefits office prior to treatment.

Managed Care

Managed care organizations, including Health Maintenance Organizations (HMOs) and Preferred Provider Organizations (PPOs), typically offer lower health care insurance premiums by controlling health care costs. They hold down costs by controlling access to providers, specialists, and services; they also authorize the duration and frequency of the services. SLPs, or the organizations they work for, must apply to be preferred providers within a particular managed care organization's "network" and negotiate a rate at which the HMO or PPO will pay them for their services. As with private insurance companies, you must verify requirements for client eligibility, coverage, type and amount of authorized visits, documentation, and limitations on treatment with the benefits office prior to treatment.

Private Pay

Given the complexities and costs (i.e., support staff training and time) involved in processing insurance claims, smaller outpatient practices sometimes do not bill insurance and accept only cash payments from the client. They provide documentation and billing information so that clients may submit a claim for reimbursement to their private insurance company. Medicaid does not reimburse clients directly for services; Medicare will but only if services are rendered in a physician's office or physician-directed clinic. Private pay is always an option when all other resources are exhausted or unavailable. Organizations may or may not be able to discount private payers to the same extent that they are able to offer network discounts to managed care organizations.

SERVICE DELIVERY

In fact, the corporate compliance office may restrict private payers from any discounts for two reasons. First, network discounts for SLP services may be available to managed care payers as part of a comprehensive service contract intended to bring a volume of additional business to the organization. Second, offering discounts to one payer (e.g., self-pay) would eliminate the concept of definitive "actual charges." Discounts have to be managed systematically and fairly within any organization. This introduces a challenge for providers or organizations seeking to establish "prepayment" arrangements, in which a private payer agrees to prepay an established fee for an established service (e.g., $5,000 prepaid for four evaluation sessions and thirty 45-minute therapy sessions over 6 months). The fees may be "discounted" since they are prepaid and do not incur costs for processing claims. Programs such as these are easier to manage with specialized services (such as accent reduction therapy) that are not covered by medical insurance; those services would not require justification of "medical necessity" or a physician's referral. When the SLP program is part of a large health care organization, the prepaid therapy "packages" may need to be sanctioned by the compliance office or by the facility's contracts (legal) department before implementation to ensure that any resulting discounts are balanced and priced comparably to all other payers.

Medicare

Administered by the Centers for Medicare and Medicaid Services (CMS), formerly the Health Care Financing Administration (HCFA), Medicare covers adults age 65 and older. Also covered are younger individuals with end-stage renal disease and persons who are deemed disabled by Social Security. Medicare has several parts.

Part A covers –

- the first 90 days of an inpatient hospital stay.
- the first 100 days in a skilled nursing facility.
- unlimited home health visits after a hospital or skilled nursing facility stay.
- hospice care.

Part B (supplemental insurance benefits) is an optional program. Beneficiaries must pay a monthly premium for coverage and a 20% co-pay for services. It covers –

- inpatient services such as therapy, after Part A coverage is exhausted.
- outpatient services (e.g., physician visits, SLP, OT, PT, diagnostic audiology).
- home health visits that do not occur after a hospital or skilled nursing facility stay.
- durable medical equipment (e.g., certain augmentative and alternative communication devices, wheelchairs).

Part C or Medicare + Choice

As an alternative to Medicare's original plan, and in an effort to expand health care options and reduce the growth rate of Medicare, Part C offers beneficiaries the option to receive their health care from a Medicare + Choice organization in their area. Medicare + Choice plans include coordinate care organizations, private fee-for-service plans, and medical savings accounts. Coordinate care organizations include traditional Health Maintenance Organizations (HMOs), Preferred Provider Organizations (PPOs), and Point-of-Service (POS) Organizations. Beneficiaries under these plans typically require referrals from their primary care physicians. Providers agree to provide services to beneficiaries in exchange for a predetermined monthly rate.

In fee-for-service plans, beneficiaries choose a private insurance plan that accepts Medicare beneficiaries and then choose a physician and hospital that participate in that plan. The insurance plan reimburses for all services, not Medicare. The beneficiary is responsible for paying any amount over what the insurance plan covers. If a beneficiary chooses a medical savings account (MSA), Medicare will pay the premium and will also contribute the amount it would pay annually for an average beneficiary. The money in the account is used to pay for services until the deductible is met. Regardless of the type of Medicare + Choice program, the plans must cover the same services that are covered under Medicare Parts A and B.

Private Practice and Medicare

Depending on the setting, Medicare uses different systems and different rates to reimburse health care providers or facilities. If you are in private practice, you cannot bill Medicare directly because Congress has not designated SLPs as independent providers of services under Medicare. In private practice, you have the following alternatives for billing your services to Medicare:

- Bill through a physician's provider number if you are employed by or contract with a physician's office.
- Follow CMS' procedures to become a rehabilitation agency, and obtain a provider number as an agency.
- Negotiate a contract with facilities such as hospitals, skilled nursing facilities, or home health agencies to be paid for services directly by the facility, which in turn receives payment from Medicare.

Prospective Payment Systems

Since the late 1970s, Medicare has progressively implemented cost containment measures. One of the first steps taken was to eliminate direct payment for each service ("fee for service") for hospital inpatients and establish per stay reimbursement rates based on diagnosis (payment based on Diagnosis Related Groups, DRGs) and later, for skilled nursing facility residents, on the severity and complexity of the client's condition. Because these steps have resulted in cost containment, commercial insurance and managed care coverage guidelines and payment rates have tended to conform to Medicare's policies and procedures. For example, the Medicare Physician Fee Schedule, which is the basis for billing Part B services, assigns payment amounts to each type of service, or "procedure," provided. In the Balanced Budget Act (BBA) of 1997, Congress required Medicare to contain costs by developing Prospective Payment Systems (PPS) instead of the earlier practice of paying "reasonable costs" incurred by the provider. The prospective payment systems vary significantly by setting.

As a result of these Prospective Payment Systems, facilities in most settings no longer receive direct payment from Medicare for the services that SLPs provide. Instead, the facility is challenged to provide care that achieves their clients' outcomes and results in discharge before the service costs exceed the Medicare payment. The determination of payment under PPS systems will be different depending upon the setting (hospital, inpatient rehabilitation facility, skilled nursing facility, home health, outpatient clinic). The time frame for payment will also vary (per session, per day, or per episode of care). In addition, the required assessment method, or tool, for determining the appropriate payment will also vary (based on factors such as the acuity, degree of impairment, type and extent of services needed, and the outcome of the service). Table 2.2 illustrates these PPS differences across settings. Table 2.3 provides an example of calculations to determine CPT payment rates in one geographical area (Alabama).

Payment for acute, inpatient services in hospitals through Medicare Part A will be reimbursed based on the patient's primary and secondary diagnoses, which means that Medicare has predetermined the expected cost to provide care based on the patient's diagnoses or Diagnosis Related Groups (DRGs). Similarly, Part A coverage in home health is calculated based on Health Resources Groups (HRGs). Inpatient rehabilitation facilities now work within a similar prospective payment system based on Rehabilitation Impairment Categories (RICs). Skilled nursing facilities (SNFs) are reimbursed based on Resource Utilization Groups or RUG-rates, based on a determination of several factors, such as the acuity, nursing, and rehabilitation needs of the patient. The measurement tool used for determining the expected costs in an inpatient rehabilitation facility is the Payment Assessment Instrument (PAI). The expected costs for care in skilled nursing facilities are based on an assessment methodology called a Minimum Data Set (MDS), and home health programs are required to use an assessment called the Outcome Assessment and Information Set (OASIS).

Table 2.2.
Medicare Prospective Payment Systems

	Hospitals— Part A	Rehabilitation Hospitals and Rehab Units in Hospitals— Part A	Skilled Nursing Facilities— Part A	SNF Part B (after 100 days)	Home Health Care— Part A	Outpatient (Part B)
Cost for Service and Prospective Payment Determined by	Diagnosis Related Groups (DRGs) (rehabilitation needs are not included)	Rehabilitation Impairment Categories (RIC)	Resource Utilization Group (RUG)	Medicare Fee Schedule	Health Resources Groups (HRGs)	Medicare Fee Schedule
Time Frame Covered by Payment	Per Episode of Care (EOC)	Per Episode of Care	Per Day	Per Session	Per Episode of Care	Per Procedure
Assessment Tool	n/a	Payment Assessment Instrument (PAI)	Minimum Data Set (MDS)	n/a	Outcome Assessment and Information Set (OASIS)	n/a

Table 2.3.
Example of Relative Value Units (RVUs) Calculated to Determine CPT Payment Rates in One Geographical Vicinity (example, Alabama)

CPT Description and Geographic Index	Work RVUs	Practice RVUs	Malpractice RVUs	Total RVUs Factor	2003 Conversion Fee	Adjusted
CPT 92507 Individual Speech-Language Treatment	0.52	1.56	0.02			
Alabama index	x0.978	x0.978	x0.978			
Alabama RVUs	0.508	+ 1.3572	+ 0.016	= 1.8807	x 36.7856	= $69.18

SERVICE DELIVERY

SLP Clinical Services Before PPS

- The greater the number of visits billed, the greater the revenue to the facility.
- Clinicians' time and salaries were factored into the facility's cost report; thus, every visit helped cover the costs of operation.

SLP Clinical Services After PPS

- Salary costs are viewed as a cost liability, so SLP staffing has become more streamlined to maximum efficiency and to hold down salary costs. For example, instead of hiring SLPs to work on a salary basis for a facility, SLPs may be hired to work as needed, so clinicians are paid only for their time to provide direct services.
- The focus of treatment has shifted to achieving maximum outcomes with fewer sessions.

Medicare Coding

Medicare's coding system is called the Healthcare Common Procedural Coding System (see coding discussion below). It includes Current Procedural Terminology (CPT) codes, which are discussed below as well as other levels of codes used for equipment, supplies, and procedures not listed or described in the CPT codes directory. The procedures you perform are listed in CPT codes, including swallowing and augmentative and alternative communication procedures. However, durable medical equipment to assist with communication (e.g., augmentative and alternative devices, artificial larynges, and voice amplifiers) is listed in HCPCS Level II codes (American Medical Association, 2003a; 2003b).

Non-Medicare payers frequently use the Medicare Physician Fee Schedule as a benchmark for setting their own payment rates. This means that even though the "payer mix" or "case mix" (percent of clients within the facility who fall into various payer categories) of Medicare clients seen in a given institution (such as a children's hospital) may be low, Medicare policies may be adopted and applied by other payers. Usually, the health care facility or organization will have established multiple contracts with commercial payers and managed care groups, such that there will be a wide range of coverage characteristics and payment arrangements within your payer mix. Some of the payment arrangements may resemble the Medicare Physician Fee Schedule; some may have contracts to pay a certain percent of billed services; some may pay only a small percent of the billed charge (Medicare) or a fixed amount for a limited number of days, and so forth. The organization's business plan takes into account the payer mix characteristics to ensure costs are covered and the program is profitable.

Local Medical Review Policies (LMRPs) or Local Coverage Decisions (LCDs)

Medicare is a federally-funded program administered regionally by insurance management groups that contract with Medicare as Fiscal Intermediaries (FIs). FIs are typically an insurance organization, such as Aetna or Blue Cross-Blue Shield, who follow Local Medical Review Policies (LMRPs) or what are now called Local Coverage Decisions (LCDs). LMRPs, or LCDs, provide more detailed information than Medicare's regulations about the local interpretation of coverage policies of payers. Although speech, language, and dysphagia services are covered by Medicare nationally, you will find that the interpretation of the coverage policies varies between regional FIs. Some claims for SLP services that are typically reimbursed by one FI may be denied by another. Clinicians and administrators should become familiar with their regional FI so that they are aware of any changes in LMRPs or LCDs and appeal policies or denials. You can find relevant LMRPs and LCDs developed by your FI at its Web site and at www.cms.hhs.gov/med/search/asp.

You can find information about specific policies, memos related to SLP services, references to the *Federal Register*, reimbursement rates, fiscal intermediary contacts, documentation requirements, covered and non-covered conditions and procedures through links and key word searches at the Web site www.medicare.gov.

Medicaid

Medicaid is jointly administered by the federal government (Centers for Medicare and Medicaid Services, CMS) and states (usually the state department of health) to provide medical assistance to low-income adults and eligible children. Medicaid includes –

- inpatient services,
- physician services,
- early and periodic screening, diagnosis, and treatment for eligible children under 21,
- contracts and service agreements for specialized services.

Each state sets its own eligibility criteria and determines the type, amount, and payment for services that will be covered. This results in significant variability from state-to-state. Medicaid is a large payer for early intervention (EI) services in the 0-3 population. Medicaid-supported early intervention services may be the "payer of last resort" in cases where a child's family has health insurance that will not cover the condition requiring SLP services. In some states, Medicaid and managed care groups negotiate contracts to provide coverage for health services. There will be state-to-state variations in coverage, eligibility determinations, case management, and the methods of implementing the Medicaid statutes,

Contracts, Service Agreements, and Other Third-Party Payers

Facilities and individuals can set up various types of contractual arrangements to provide services to a third party. For example, if a public school system is unable to meet the mandates of the Individuals with Disabilities Education Act (IDEA) for children with certain communication disorders, then the school may have a contract, or service agreement, with an organization that is staffed and equipped to provide services for children with those conditions (e.g., autism, velopharyngeal dysfunction, severe speech or language delays, feeding and swallowing.) (See Appendix D for an example of a Community Clinic Service Agreement.)

In that circumstance, the service provider organization must comply with the stipulations of the contract with regard to –

- **documentation** – the contractor may want to have periodic, narrative progress reports of the sort not typically required by insurance companies;
- **accountability** – the contractor may require the clinician to track all time spent in providing services, including travel, therapy preparation, phone calls;
- **nature of the service** – the contractor may require that the clinician participate in the Individualized Family Service Plan (IFSP) process in the case of early intervention (EI) services or in Individualized Education Plan (IEP) meetings for school-aged children.

Coding

All of the reimbursement systems described above mandate that codes accurately reflect the client's diagnosis and the clinical procedures provided. Accurate coding of procedures and diagnoses is essential to ensure that claims can be processed and the organization is properly paid for its services. Like all health care providers, you must account for what you did (e.g., the procedures you performed) and how those procedures relate to a documented medical diagnosis. Many payers ask the clinician to account for how the service relates to the medical condition of the client and to provide justification for the "medical necessity" of a procedure.

The universally accepted system for documenting clinical procedures in the United States is the Current Procedural Terminology or CPT codes. Developed and published by the American Medical Association (AMA, 2003a; 2003b), CPT codes describe procedures that are performed. CPTs are also referred to as "Level I" HCPCS codes, referring to the AMA's system of 5 digit codes with 2 digit modifiers (Healthcare Common Procedure Coding System, or HCPCS, pronounced "hick-picks"), (discussed above, see Medicare). CPTs are the primary method of describing, coding, and reporting services performed. The AMA publishes a revised edition of the CPT codes, generally yearly, with additions, deletions, corrections, and changes in modifier coding. To verify the most up-to-date CPTs for

SLP procedures, clinicians can consult the most recent version of the AMA's Current Procedural Terminology manual, or go to www.ama-assn.org/cpt or the ASHA Web site, www.asha.org.

Whereas the AMA's CPTs are Level I HCPCS codes, Medicare/Medicaid has Level II HCPCS codes that identify equipment and supplies as well as clinical procedures that are not included in the CPT System. Level II codes are also used by other health plans. This system uses a single alphabet letter followed by 4-digit codes that are grouped by the type of service or supply provided. HCPCS codes may be required by Medicare for a procedure that has not yet been assigned a CPT code by the AMA.

> Accurate coding of procedures and diagnoses is essential...so claims can be processed and the organization paid for its services.

Payers determine independently the amount they will pay for each code. Clinicians bear a professional and ethical responsibility to code accurately the procedures they perform without being influenced by the amounts the code may reimburse. Payment rates for CPT codes in the Medicare Physician Fee Schedule are derived from a formula involving several factors.

Physician Fee Schedule

- Relative Value Units (see below)
- Geographic Index (rates vary in different parts of the country)
- Conversion Factor (adjusted annually by CMS)

Components of Relative Value Units

- Physician work (reflects any physician involvement in the procedure; this component increases the payment rate for the procedure.)
- Practice expense (based on the average time SLPs spend performing the procedure)
- Malpractice expense

Types of CPT Codes

- **Untimed codes**. Regardless of the length of the session, untimed codes can only be billed by the procedure or session, rather than by the time spent to provide the service. A 60-minute treatment session with an adult with aphasia and a 30-minute session with a child with a language delay will each be billed as CPT code 92507 (speech-language treatment). A 4-hour evaluation session with a child will be billed as a 92506 "comprehensive evaluation" procedure, as will a 1-hour dysarthria assessment. Most codes used by SLPs are untimed codes.

- **Timed Codes**. Timed codes can be billed for multiple units, usually 15 minutes each, according to the amount of time the clinician spent with the client. For example, a physical therapist working on strengthening exercises with the client for 30 minutes can bill two units of CPT code 97530 for therapeutic exercise. An aphasia evaluation, CPT 96105, is specified as a 60-minute, or timed, procedure, so if the evaluation required 2 hours, 2 procedures could be billed. The rub is that some payers may only reimburse one, or the first, 96105 coded procedure regardless of the time required.

- **Modifiers**. Medicare requires the use of modifiers to designate the profession of the provider (GN for SLPs, GO for occupational therapists, and GP for physical therapists) and to designate when a given procedure varies from the standard. These modifiers and the restrictions on their use will be provided in the current version of the CPT manual.

- **Bundled Codes**. Multiple procedures billed on a given day may be subject to particular scrutiny. Medicare's Correct Coding Initiative (CCI) establishes coding "edits" that are used by Medicare and other payers to review claims electronically and identify codes that are improperly "bundled" (i.e., specific procedures that are actually part of a more comprehensive procedure code that has also been charged). Such charging practices will result in denial of claims. For example, a physical therapy procedure such as "aquatic therapy" (97113) cannot be billed on the same date of service as the more comprehensive procedure "therapeutic exercise" (97530). Other CCI edits prohibit billing for dysphagia evaluation (92610) on the same day as instrumental assessments (92611, 92613, or 92616) unless a "modifier" (-59) is attached to the instrumental assessment CPT code. The -59 modifier indicates that the second procedure is distinct from the first procedure. CCI edits are subject to periodic updating. These changes should be monitored by the facility's billing department as will claim denials resulting from CCI edits. (Relevant CCI edits can be found on ASHA's Web site).

International Classification of Diseases (ICD)

ICD codes were developed by the World Health Organization (WHO) to refer to the diseases and conditions that cause the need for medical services, including SLP (ICD-9-CM Code Book for Physicians, 2003). For example, ICD coding of a hospital patient by a medical records technician might include –

- the primary medical diagnosis (e.g., CVA, 437.1),
- related conditions (e.g., hypertension, 401.0),
- resulting conditions (e.g., dysphagia, 438.82, aphasia, late effect of cerebrovascular disease 438.11).

The diagnosis must include the primary diagnosis and any additional diagnoses related to the medical condition for which SLP services are being provided. Medicare asks for medical diagnoses to be coded at the highest level of specificity to the treatment (i.e., "dysphagia" would be preferable as the primary diagnosis for a SLP evaluating or treating swallowing, not "CVA," even though stroke may be the condition that caused the dysphagia. "CVA," or 437.1, can be listed as the second diagnosis). If the client also had an additional, unrelated medical condition, such as an orthopedic or skin disorder, these diagnoses would not be included because they did not relate to the SLP treatment. Clinicians should code diagnoses completely and accurately to reflect the reason for the services or risk reimbursement denials, and clinicians should code as closely to the actual condition or disorder they are treating. For example, if you are evaluating a feeding and swallowing disorder in a child with Down Syndrome, you would code the diagnosis closest to the condition you are treating, i.e., "dysphagia" and not "Down Syndrome." Despite accurate coding, certain diagnoses will not appear under the "covered" conditions for a given payer for SLP services or are simply problematic for insurance coverage, so payment may be denied (see earlier discussion regarding preauthorization and predetermination).

Documentation for Reimbursement

Writing accurate and descriptive, yet streamlined, documentation is as important as the service you actually deliver to your clients. Documentation provides the only tangible evidence of the nature of the service, the date the service was provided, who provided it, why, and to whom. Documentation is the only record of the benefit of the SLP service and the only way a claims processor (who has never laid eyes on the client and may know next to nothing about the disorder being treated) can judge if the evaluation or treatment had any benefit. Although time spent documenting is not directly reimbursed, the time spent providing treatment is also not likely to be reimbursed without it! Payment for services may be denied if the documentation does not provide a clear explanation of why the services were needed, what services were provided, who provided them, when they provided them, and how the client made functional improvement as a result of the services. Most payers require a written "plan of care" that establishes functional and measurable goals prior to the initiation of services. Clearly conceived and developed written goals of treatment and subsequent progress notes will help in communicating progress related to that plan. Good documentation also helps when advocating for clients and families and communicating within teams and with case managers.

The Basics of Documentation

Capturing Charges

Some SLPs think documentation is limited only to clinical documentation, such as notes in the medical record and reports of evaluation, treatment, and discharge plans. However, depending on the processes adopted by a particular practice or facility, you have additional documentation requirements that are equally important in order for the clients' records and billing information to be handled smoothly and to avoid delays or denials in processing for reimbursement. When completing charge form information, you must accurately record (either in handwritten or electronic form) all required information, such as the client's identifying information, the date of service, the time spent with the client, the procedures (by charge code or CPT codes) provided, and who provided the service. The written or electronic signature and discipline of the clinician are also typically required. If a client or payer questions whether a service was provided on a particular day, a cumulative record of dates and procedures is critical. This record may be kept in an electronic database in the billing office.

Superbills

Private practitioners may generate a "superbill" (see Appendix E, Model Superbill for Speech-Language Pathology), which provides a cumulative list of procedures and charges, along with ICD codes and other information typically required by insurance carriers. Private pay clients can then use the superbill as their billing statement or forward it to their insurance to request reimbursement.

Procedure Coding

In some cases, clinicians complete a billing form that will capture the service data so that it can be transferred to a billing claim or entered into a cumulative electronic billing record for the client. The form will usually have a place to indicate the primary diagnosis and other diagnoses pertinent to the visit (see previous discussion regarding Coding, Medicare, and ICDs), as that information will be required for claim processing and will contain a list of procedures that are coded by CPTs or some other coding system used by the facility. Most facilities have a Charge Master (CM), or Charge Description Master (CDM), which is the composite list of all of the procedures, charges, professional service fees, technical fees, and supply charges of that institution. Encounter forms sometimes have a "charge code" that is electronically linked to a CPT or HCPCS, so clinicians need only check the charge code without having to refer to its CPT. Increasingly, organizations are moving to automated charge capture, in which clinicians use a computerized system to record a visit and that system automatically links to the appropriate charge on the billing account. These kinds of time saving systems are discussed in Chapter 6, Technology.

> Key information should be summarized or easily identifiable under the appropriate headings.

Clinical Documentation

Your clinical documentation must meet the needs of different types of readers, each of whom must be able to find the information they need as expediently as possible. Physicians and other health care professionals read the SLP's documentation to gather a clinical picture of the client and the functional goals and progress the client has made. In today's health care environment, few professionals have time to read a multiple-page narrative report. Key information should be summarized or easily identifiable under the appropriate headings.

Nonclinical employees, insurance claims processors, and medical records technicians are trained to recognize specific pieces of information and process claims if the information matches the coverage and reimbursement guidelines set by the payer. If the report contains confusing clinical jargon or abbreviations, if it is missing required pieces of information, or if it is illegible, the claim either may not be processed or may be denied. Insurers must see evidence of progress toward goals. For more on efficient documentation, see Chapter 6, Technology.

Documenting the Need for Treatment

An evaluation report needs to answer the questions posed by other professionals, families, and insurance claims processors.

What functional deficits does the client have as a result of mild aphasia/severe aphonia/moderate dysarthria/severe phonologic disorder?

Deficits that can compromise the client's safety or activities of daily living have a strong function component. For example, although the client's mild aphasia interferes with social interaction, a stronger rationale for treatment is that the communication impairment also interferes with the client's ability to read the medication schedule, communicate with doctors during medical appointments, or call for emergency assistance.

How does the communication deficit relate to the diagnosed medical condition(s)? For example, a client who is referred for swallowing problems following coronary artery bypass surgery may need to have a physician provide a diagnosis of dysphagia, because the correlation of heart surgery to swallowing problems may not be widely recognized by reviewers. Similarly, a client who is referred for cognitive-communication problems following hospitalization for hip surgery may be denied coverage for SLP services unless there is a recent diagnosis of neurologic problems. In some cases, you may have to communicate with the physician to make sure that an appropriate related medical diagnosis has been made.

Is there a reasonable expectation that treatment can improve clients' functioning in an area of life that affects their safety or daily activities? For example, the case cannot be made that treatment 3 times a week for 3 months will improve the memory of a client with early Alzheimer's disease. However, you can make a case that several treatment sessions involving the caregiver and client to develop strategies to modify the environment and cue the client will reduce levels of agitation and decrease the likelihood of engaging in unsafe activities.

Are steps being taken to ensure cost containment? Documentation should attempt to predict or define the time frame encompassed in the treatment.

Functionally Relevant Goals

Once the justification for the diagnosis and treatment for the communication disorder have been established, the long- and short-term goals should specifically identify the functional improvement that the client is expected to make. Goals must be written to satisfy the requirements and obligations specified by the payers.

Goal Writing "Do's and Don'ts"

- Don't make goals too general, for example "Improve word finding."
- Don't set goals based on clinical activities, for example "Will remember four objects with 5 minute delay." "Will repeat word lists with the initial /s/ sound with 90% accuracy."
- Do make goals measurable AND functional, for example "Client will eat a complete 6-oz serving of pudding in 10 minutes without coughing or choking, using compensatory strategies with minimal verbal cuing." Or "Client will use Memory Log to record the morning's therapy activities and accurately report back at least five therapy activities." Or "Client will read and/or point to pictures on a restaurant menu to indicate what he and his wife had for dinner the previous evening, with 90% accuracy."

Appealing Denials

Payers deny claims for a variety of good and not-so-good reasons. For example,

- predetermination or preauthorization verification of coverage benefits did not occur prior to service.
- the physician failed to sign or date the order.
- the physician was not the Primary Care Provider (PCP).
- the claims adjustor disagreed with the physician's determination of medical necessity.

Claims can also be denied if the documentation does not provide a justification for the service. Many payers, such as Medicare, will deny claims that are not submitted in a timely manner. Facilities may ultimately opt to "write off" denied claims. In many cases, however, the facility will be notified that additional information is needed to process the claim, and payment may be worth pursuing. In the case of insurance, a claim that is denied as not covered by the benefits will go back to the client or family. They then may recheck their policy benefits and EOB for the date of service and ask the facility or clinician for assistance with advocating for coverage and resubmitting the claim. If the facility has inaccurately informed the client that coverage was authorized or failed to inform the client that authorization does not guarantee payment will be made by the insurer, the client may refuse payment. The facility may then need to provide evidence of predetermination or preauthorization and resubmit the claim or submit the claim to a higher level of reviewer or a legal adjudicator. It is important to remember that if insurance does not pay for a service, then clients or families most likely will be billed. Failure to obtain reimbursement will influence the client's or family's satisfaction with the service and the perception of quality. (See Appendix F, Justification for Treatment and Appendix G, Appeal of Denied Claim for sample letters.)

References and Resources for Appeals

Each payer has an appeals process that can be used by either the client or the payer to contest a denied claim. In some cases, you may need to provide testimony and research articles to justify your services to individuals or provide outcomes data to show the benefits of treatment. ASHA's National Outcomes Measurement System (NOMS) (ASHA, 2002b) is one way of obtaining outcomes data. You or the SLPs in your department can contribute your client information and outcomes to ASHA's national database using Functional Communication Measures (FCMs). The database yields data that are facility-specific outcomes reports as well as national outcome data. ASHA works with various networks of SLPs to coordinate advocacy activities nationally or within states. One advocacy network resource is the State Advocates for Reimbursement (STAR) and another is the National Insurance Advocacy Initiative (NIAI). (See also Chapter 9, Advocacy.) In addition, your state may have a health insurance arbitration panel that will rule on your insurance denial.

An Ounce of Prevention is Worth a Pound of Appeal Documentation

Good documentation and attention to coverage guidelines help prevent denials, which cost you and your administrative staff time and money to reprocess. If you work in a small practice, it is especially important to receive payment for claims in a timely fashion so you can pay other fixed expenses (salaries, rent, heat, electricity) that are due on a monthly basis. Otherwise, you will experience cash flow problems. In almost any setting, the organization has already paid the cost to provide service long before it receives any payment. It is far preferable to prevent the denial in the first place than to add costs by appealing it. Therefore, efforts to receive the fullest possible reimbursement in the quickest amount of time (preventing submission delays and denials) will help to maintain a flow of sufficient operating income to provide services to present and future clients. In any setting, efficiencies in documentation work flow are essential time savers. Table 2.4 describes a work flow process analysis for the administrative steps involved in evaluating a new client. Table 2.5 demonstrates a simplified process that minimizes the time and effort by the SLP.

Table 2.4.
Example of a Work Flow Process Analysis

Objective	Record of Task Sequence	By?	Time?	Needed?
Schedule and complete initial evaluation of a new client.	1. MD order for "speech tx" received via fax, signed by nurse.	Support staff	1 min	Yes
	2. Logged into referral clinic's database.	Support staff	10 min	No
	3. Clinic file made.	Support Staff	10 min	No
	4. File placed in clinician's intake box for first available appointment.	Support Staff	2 min	No
	5. Request sent to family for release of information.	Clinician	15 min	Yes
	6. Phone call to family for insurance information.	Clinician	10 min	Yes
	7. Appointment scheduled on clinician's calendar.	Clinician	5 min	Yes
	8. Contacted benefits office to verify coverage and obtain authorization.	Clinician	15 min	Yes
	9. Contacted Centralized Medical Records to assign Medical Record to new client.	Support Staff	1 min	Yes
	10. Phoned MD office to amend original order per authorization requirements (benefits office requires medical diagnosis, stated duration of tx, and MD signature).	Clinician	10 min	Yes
	11. Received and filed revised faxed order.	Support Staff	5 min	Yes
	12. Phoned family to schedule appointment.	Clinician	10 min	Yes
	13. Sent medical/social history intake form to family.	Clinician	10 min	No
	14. Reviewed medical records.	Clinician	30 min	Yes
	15. Clinic intake form received and reviewed in preparation for visit.	Clinician	30 min	No
	16. Medical history information reviewed prior to visit.	Clinician	10 min	Yes
	17. Medical orders and history records copied for clinic chart prior to routing original documents to Medical Center's Medical Records Department.	Clinician	10 min	No
	18. Client seen for evaluation.	Clinician	45 min	Yes
	19. Encounter form completed.	Clinician	1 min	Yes
	20. Encounter form routed to Patient Accounting.	Support staff	5 min	Yes
	21. Client report dictated.	Clinician	30 min	Yes
	22. Client report typed, copied and filed in Centralized Medical Record, original sent to referring physician.	Support Staff	15 min	Yes

Analysis = Over 4.5 Hours to Complete Tasks

Table 2.5.
Example of Work Flow Process Simplification

Objective	Record of Task Sequence	By?	Time?	Needed?
Schedule and complete initial evaluation of a new client.	1. MD order for "speech tx" received via fax, signed by nurse	Support staff	1 min	Yes
	2. Intake packet mailed to family containing a. release of information (ROI); b. request for insurance coverage information; c. clinic medical/social history intake form, d. family e-mail address; e. return envelope with postage paid; and f. phone number of centralized scheduling office of SLP clinic at Medical Center with scheduling instructions.	Support staff	5 min	Yes
	3. Contacted benefits office to obtain verification of coverage and authorization of visit.	Support Staff	15 min	Yes
	4. Clinic's automated "physician's order form" sent to referring MD (faxed electronically to office e-mail address) requesting a. revised MD order (per benefits office specific requirements) and b. all pertinent medical records (pending receipt of ROI from family) faxed to clinic.	Support Staff	5 min	Yes
	5. Revised MD order received via fax.	Support Staff	5 min	Yes
	6. Family contacted centralized scheduler for appointment; scheduler assigned a medical record number and entered insurance and other pertinent data into centralized medical record; scheduler advised family to arrive 15 minutes ahead of appointment and to bring insurance card and a completed clinic medical/social history intake form to initial visit.	Centralized Scheduler	0 min	Yes
	7. MD order and copies of medical history information scanned into client's Centralized Medical Record.	Support Staff	5 min	Yes
	8. Clinic intake form information reviewed by clinician with the family during intake interview.	Clinician	15 min	Yes
	9. Client seen for evaluation of communication.	Clinician	45 min	Yes
	10. Report of initial results and recommendations documented via computerized template linked automatically to Patient Accounting.	Clinician	10 min	Yes
	11. Automatic charge submitted to Patient Accounting.	Clinician	0 min	Yes

Analysis = Approximately 1.5 Hours to Complete Tasks

Resource Utilization

In this climate of cost cutting and reduced benefits by health insurance plans, you are challenged to design a treatment plan that will result in functionally useful outcomes for clients in a relatively short period of time or with only a few treatment sessions. From the initiation of treatment, you need to think about transitioning services at discharge or at the end of the authorized plan. This process can start early by engaging family members or significant others in the treatment sessions so they can help with coaching and cuing communication and with carryover activities at home.

Clients who have additional resources may elect to pay out of pocket for continued services after their health benefits have expired; however, most clients cannot afford to continue with treatment after insurance benefits are exhausted. You will need to plan how to achieve the maximum benefit of each session and to help the client find other available resources (e.g., group treatment, community support groups, volunteers). A word of caution regarding the option of clients paying out of pocket for additional services: According to ASHA's Code of Ethics, treatment should only be provided when benefits can reasonably be expected.

In many cases, the covered services may fall short of the client's actual needs and potential to benefit from therapy. Some amount of *pro bono* (unpaid) service may be provided, but the costs need to be offset by a positive operating margin (see discussion of Profit Centers at the beginning of this chapter). Facilities, even those underwritten by private or public funds, cannot afford to provide unlimited, free, or low cost services for all who want it. Most organizations and agencies have eligibility criteria and priorities to help limited resources meet demands. In health care settings, the health insurance coverage of the client or family, as well as any other eligible funding opportunities, is also limited. Compliance rules may limit the extent of pro bono service that can be provided.

Obtaining coverage for treatment for pediatric services is especially challenging, particularly if the "medical necessity" for the service is ambiguous. Clinicians in pediatric health care institutions must tap all available children's services programs and partner with the state's early childhood intervention services, Head Start, and public schools in the provision of services. This may require spending some part of the (authorized) covered clinical services to train preschool or school-based SLP providers in treatment services to a given client.

Ethical Service Delivery

The competition for health care dollars and emphasis on efficiency and cost savings may result in situations where business pressures seem to be at conflict with professional ethics. Ethical practice reduces risk to the employer organization and is good business practice.

Clinical departments may report to nonclinical administrators who look at SLPs and their services primarily from a business perspective. Administrators may not recognize that quality of services would be compromised by certain changes. SLPs who provided services under the previous "fee-for-service" systems may feel ethically compromised when limited resources necessitate what seems to be "rationing" of care. Or they may feel that being held accountable for productivity targets and billable hours is incompatible with their professional ethics. Clinicians in their first jobs may feel they are not in a position to question practices and may comply with requirements that seem to be unethical. ASHA's Code of Ethics offers clinicians answers and guidance to the question, "Is this practice ethical?"

Ethical practice requires familiarity with ASHA's Code of Ethics (ASHA, 2003) and the general coverage rules of payers as well as the ability to apply them critically to analyze a particular situation. ASHA's Code of Ethics provides general guidelines, and *Issues in Ethics* statements published by ASHA's Board of Ethics clarify particular situations (e.g., *Drawing Cases for Private Practice from Primary Place of Employment*, ASHA, 2002c). But some practices are not always entirely clear-cut, and ASHA's policy documents do not provide answers for every situation. Chapter 4, Standards and Compliance covers this area more fully; however, a few cautions are indicated here.

The legal and/or ethical principles at play in SLP clinical practices are clear about the following practices:

- **You may not falsify clinical records**. A medical record is a legal document. No one may erase, edit, or remove an entry in the medical record. You should refuse any requests to alter a diagnosis, backdate records, or change dates of service or time spent to increase reimbursement or to comply retrospectively with coverage guidelines. Corrections to a record can only be made by drawing a line through the error (not obliterating it) and initialing the correction with the date of the correction.

- **You may not commit fraud**. You may not claim to have provided services that you did not provide or in any other way misrepresent yourself or your activities to obtain reimbursement. That means that a clinician cannot document or bill for any service or time frame of service that was not actually provided.

- **You must adhere to guidelines for supervision of noncertified individuals**. Having graduate students do a clinical practicum in a health care facility can be a time-consuming but valuable recruiting tool. SLP assistants can also be valuable as care extenders; however, neither group can perform independently. SLPs must comply with the most stringent of ASHA's, the state's, and the payer's guidelines for supervision. Just as medical training programs prohibit medical students from writing notes for the attending (supervising staff) physician, individuals who are not qualified to practice speech-language pathology will have certain limits on their clinical activities. In some settings, student SLPs, as a part of their practicum, may provide treatment that is entirely directed and supervised by a licensed SLP and may be allowed to write notes "as a scribe for" (and co-signed by) the licensed SLP. Such practices are allowable if the corporate compliance office of the facility concurs. However, if the SLP were asked to sign off on the treatment plans written by noncertified individuals, that would not be ethical. ASHA's Code of Ethics prohibits this behavior.

- **Most referral agreements are illegal**. Health care providers may not negotiate referral agreements with other entities (e.g., physicians' offices) for the purpose of increasing business. A clinical reason should be the basis for referring a client to a specific practitioner, not an economic reason. The SLP could be penalized for receiving a kickback, which may be anything of value, in exchange for a referral. Taken a step further, the corporate compliance officer may object to allowing clinicians or facilities to offer a "free" service, if it appears to be an inducement for referrals.

Less clear-cut ethical dilemmas occur when conflicts arise between institutional policies and a clinician's personal standard of clinical practice, especially with regard to the clinician's clinical competencies. For example, a radiologist may decide against participating in modified barium swallows (MBS) because the amount of reimbursement does not justify the cost of time. One SLP may feel confident determining when to ask for a consultation and show the radiologist the tape of the MBS; another SLP may feel that client care is potentially compromised by the absence of a radiologist and decline to perform the MBS alone. In another example, an administrator may set a standard that evaluations must be scheduled to last no more than 30 minutes. One SLP may feel that, with rare exceptions, this is an inadequate amount of time for evaluation and that it is inappropriate interference with clinical judgment by a nonqualified provider.

When such conflicts occur, you should be aware of clinical practice standards and benchmarks at other similar facilities. You can consult with ASHA to see if there are professional policies that guide your actions. For example, SLPs can no longer claim that writing four-page typed narrative reports is the accepted practice standard. Although we might like the luxury of taking the time to write long reports, most facilities have modified their documentation requirements both because referring physicians do not want to read them and the facility would rather see the clinicians spend time doing more productive activities. Consequently, a clinician would have a difficult time defending the "right" to schedule time to write lengthy reports.

Summary

The business side of health care encompasses aspects of practice that you may not have considered before entering the profession. In today's environment, however, understanding the business side of clinical service is essential to the effective use of the clinician's time and the client's available resources. The business side of service delivery focuses on efficiencies and cost-savings, which are crucial to meeting budgeted productivity targets, organizational performance, and job security regardless of where we work. Good business practices in clinical service delivery will help to protect the financial solvency of the practice or organization. Good business practices should not require clinicians "to do more with less," but rather to spend work time as productively as possible. To apply business practices in service delivery, clinicians should understand the requirements and expectations for eligibility and coverage for their services. Clinicians need to ensure accurate coding and maintain conscientious, but streamlined, documentation. The business side of clinical services must conform to ethical behavioral expectations for the profession, as contained in the ASHA Code of Ethics.

References

American Medical Association. (2003a). *Current procedural terminology*. (Standard ed.). Atlanta, GA: AMA Press.

American Medical Association. (2003b). *Healthcare common procedure coding system*. Atlanta, GA: AMA Press.

American Speech-Language-Hearing Association. (2003). Code of ethics (rev.). *ASHA Supplement 23*, 13-15.

American Speech-Language-Hearing Association. (2002a). *Report of the ASHA speech-language pathology health care survey*. Rockville, MD: Author.

American Speech-Language-Hearing Association. (2002b). *Gaining the support of your staff and administration: Health care*. Rockville, MD: Author.

American Speech-Language-Hearing Association. (2002c). Drawing cases for private practice from primary place of employment. *ASHA Supplement 22*, 69-70.

ICD - 9 CM Code Book for Physicians. (2003). (6th ed., Vols 1-2). Reston, VA: St. Anthony Publishers, INGENIX.

SERVICE DELIVERY

Chapter 3
Financial
Management

Every business must conduct its affairs in a financially responsible manner. Most organizations operate within a budget, and thus, function within the accounting and fiscal principles of a business. This is true regardless of their funding sources or their for-profit or not-for-profit status. Although administrators are ultimately responsible for the financial operations of an organization or unit, clinicians must work in partnership with them to ensure the financial viability of the organization.

Chapter Focus
Finance and accounting are the language of business. In this chapter, you will be introduced to financial terms, measures, and concepts that can give you a picture of the financial health of an organization. We will examine **profit motive**, **budgets**, **revenue** and **costs**, types of **corporations** and **accounting**.

Learning Outcomes
Interpret financial statements.

Identify Generally Accepted Accounting Principles.

Read and interpret ledger and journal entries.

Use basic accounting principles.

Profit Motive
Speech-language pathologists (SLPs) often have an aversion to discussing profit in relation to the delivery of professional services. These discussions may be seen as inappropriate, irrelevant, or simply distasteful. Despite the stigma associated with the idea of generating profit from delivering professional services, SLPs need to understand that a profit motive is considered to be the foundation of business.

The Internal Revenue Service considers a profit motive to be the way to determine whether or not an individual or entity is actually engaged in business. You don't necessarily need to generate revenue, since some businesses indeed lose money, but there needs to be a motive or a plan to generate a profit (so you can pay taxes). Even not-for profit organizations need to take in more money than they spend. These organizations typically derive much of their revenue from charitable contributions, grants, or other sources of funds. Regardless of the source of funds, they need to take in more money than they spend in order to continue operating.

Budgets

Budgets are used to project revenue (income) and expenses (costs) for an entity over a specific period, usually a fiscal year. A fiscal year can be calculated within the calendar year (January through December) or within another 12-month time frame (e.g., July 1st through June 30th). The time spent in the budgeting process will vary depending on the setting, the number of employees, and the variety and complexity of the services. A solo practitioner will spend less time in this process than a corporate director of rehabilitation for a large hospital system. The process and the budget itself are no less important in either setting. The planning and thought processes for large and small budgets are equally important, and both can be time consuming.

The purpose of a budget is to arrive at the most accurate picture possible of how much it will cost to provide a service and how much the business will likely make or lose during the budgeted period. The following questions about revenue and expenses might be considered when developing a budget.

Making Widgets and Providing Health Care Services: A Business Comparison

Widget Store	SLP Department
Sells product for money.	Sells service for money.
Produces enough widgets to meet budget projections.	Provides enough service to meet budget projections.
Pays for salary, benefits, supplies, overhead.	Pays for salary, benefits, supplies, overhead.
Makes a profit to continue making widgets.	Makes a profit to continue providing service.
Sells widgets at sufficient quality and at a price that is competitive.	Provides a skilled service that must be of equal or higher quality than other programs and priced competitively.

Revenue

- What are your current sources of revenue?
- Are you changing any revenue sources?
- Are some revenue sources more profitable than others?
- Can you increase profit by eliminating some sources of revenue in favor of others?
- How long does it take to collect on accounts and what are the problem areas in your "accounts receivable?" Do you need to borrow on a line of credit to cover cash shortfalls?

- Are revenues cyclical in nature? Can you plan ahead to have some revenue sources pick up when others decrease?
- Can you generate more revenue with your current resources if they are used more effectively (e.g., by improving productivity)?

Expenses

- What are your current costs of doing business (salary, fringes, facility costs)?
- Are you planning to make changes that will affect costs?
- Do you have any long-term liabilities (e.g., loans or equipment leases) that will mature in the coming period?
- Are you expecting any increases for overhead or fringes (e.g., utilities, rent, medical, dental)?
- What pay raises are likely to be awarded this coming period?
- Are there any new programs or initiatives that need funding?
- Are there programs or initiatives that no longer need funding?
- Is there an opportunity to trim any excess from your largest cost centers?
- Are there capital expenditures (e.g., new technologies) that will likely pay off in lower costs or higher revenue in the future?
- Is money being spent wisely? That is, if it were your own money, would you spend it this way?

Many organizations require budget information to be completed and presented to the financial manager or management office. A budget proposal can take different forms depending on the organization. It can be as simple as a form or as complex as a business plan or formal proposal. Other organizations require complete cost-benefit analysis and rationale for budget figures and projections. The most important aspect of a budget is how realistic it is.

Budgeting can take a great deal of time and energy, but in the end, it is merely a projection based on the best available information. Budgets are forward-looking reports based on review of previous financial data and trends within the data. Each period (monthly, quarterly, or annually) a comparison is made between the actual and budgeted revenue and expenses to determine budget variances. Just as managers look at their budget variances periodically to determine how accurate their budgeting was, you need to consider where your actual expenditures varied from the previous budget. Doing this regularly will help you make decisions and sharpen your ability to anticipate, plan, and budget in the future.

Expenses

As with any business, there are costs associated with providing speech-language pathology services. Different settings will allocate expenses in different ways. For example, a solo practice would likely show all expenses coming from the main operating budget; a hospital may show certain expenses, such as recruiting or marketing, coming from multiple departmental budgets. Regardless of how they are allocated, expenses can be broken down into a few general categories.

Recurring fixed costs. These are costs that do not change from month to month. Examples of recurring fixed costs include –

- rent or mortgage,
- loan or lease payments,
- other items such as Internet broadband connection, Yellow Pages advertising.

Recurring variable costs. These are costs that recur each month but vary slightly from month-to- month, such as –

- telephone bill,
- gas and electric,
- supply and material purchases.

Direct costs. These are costs that are directly related to the clinician providing the service, including –

- staff salary or contract rate,
- fringe benefits,
- accrued time off.

Indirect costs. These are costs that are incurred per clinician but not necessarily related directly to the provision of service. They may include –

- mileage reimbursement,
- continuing education,
- institutional costs (particularly in universities),
- professional liability or general liability insurance,
- administrator or supervisor salaries (fixed and variable),
- marketing and advertising,
- information technology,
- publication subscriptions.

Each business will categorize and track its costs in a way that makes sense for that particular entity. The above categories are widely recognized, but different settings warrant different cost categories. Clearly, there are many more costs involved in providing professional services beyond the clinician's salary. In some settings, the other costs of doing business (indirect costs) are greater than the direct costs.

Revenue

Revenue is the money generated from business activity. Revenue is generally derived from providing clinical services and receiving payment directly from the client, an insurance company, or a government supported program like Medicaid or Medicare. However, the business of speech-language pathology can also generate revenue in other ways. Fundraising, writing grants, hosting continuing education activities, providing expert testimony in court cases, and publishing a proprietary set of materials are examples of other ways to generate revenue.

> Careful documentation is critical to collecting your services.

Productivity refers to some measurement of efficiency of a clinician, program, department, or organization in delivering products or services (see Chapter 2, Service Delivery). In a business sense, that efficiency is measured by the amount of revenue generated by a clinician, combined with the other necessary activities associated with generating that revenue (e.g., documentation, meetings). Each setting will have a productivity standard based on its cost structure. Clinicians need to produce (i.e., provide billable services) to the extent that what they bill covers all costs and generates a profit margin. It's not enough to bill an amount equal to what is paid in salaries, since this will actually result in a net loss when the other costs of doing business are considered.

Generating revenue is important, but it is just as important to be successful in collecting money. If a clinician's productivity generates $2,000 in billable activity in a week, but only 20% is collected for various reasons (e.g., incomplete or tardy documentation, poor authorization management), then the total billable amount is inconsequential. Generating and collecting revenue are both important aspects of the income side of running a business.

Careful documentation is critical in collecting on services billed (accounts receivable). Documenting clinical activity in a manner that will allow for timely payment for services is an important responsibility for clinicians (see Chapter 2, Service Delivery). Some common reasons for collection problems include –

- missing information in documentation (diagnosis, procedure, signature, credentials, etc.).
- missing a submission deadline that causes the claim to be paid in the next period.
- beginning services before an authorization is obtained.

- providing services after the end date of an authorization.
- exceeding the number of authorized visits.

Pricing

SLPs frequently ask what to charge for their professional services, and the answer will vary among settings. The best way to set a price, or fee, is to calculate the cost of providing the service, and add your margin. It is often difficult to figure the actual costs involved in providing one therapy session, one evaluation, or one hour of professional service. To do this, it is best to use a period of one week or one month and work backwards from there. To understand what an appropriate fee would be, consider the following:

- What are the costs per unit of service?
- How many services are provided in the period represented by the costs? For example, if you were to do one endoscopy per month, then the cost per unit of service is high due to the need to capture the cost for the use of the equipment. If you were to do 120 endoscopies per month, the costs would be lower as the equipment is being utilized more fully. Furthermore, if the SLP is less productive, the cost per unit of service is higher than if the SLP is more productive, because the salary costs stay the same.
- What is the expected profit margin?

Just to illustrate, assume the following represents the cost of doing business for a small clinic with two clinicians and a part-time support person:

	Annually	**Weekly (52)**	**Daily**
Recurring Fixed (e.g., rent)	$30,000.00	$576.92	$115.38
Recurring Variable (e.g., utilities)	13,000.00	250.00	50.00
Direct (e.g., personnel and benefits)	150,000.00	2,884.62	576.92
Indirect (e.g., insurance)	12,000.00	230.77	46.15
Total Costs	*$205,000.00*	*$3,942.31*	*$788.45*

Let's say that each clinician will render 25 billable hours per week and that the clinic needs a 30% margin to stay in business. The actual productivity standard and profit margin are determined by the unique circumstances of each entity.

Weekly Productivity	Hours
Clinician 1	25
Clinician 2	25
Total	*50*

Profit Margin   30.00%

By taking the weekly cost of $3,942.31 and dividing by the total number of billable hours the clinicians expect to render in a week, we arrive at the clinic's break-even fee of $78.85 per hour. By adding the expected margin of 30% (78.85 x .30), we arrive at an hourly fee, based on their costs and margin.

Breakeven	$78.85
Profit Margin	$23.65
Total Hourly Fee	*$102.50*

Other Pricing Considerations

The above example appears to work on paper, but in the real world, it has some limitations.

The clinicians won't render 25 billable hours every single week of the year. Sick time, holidays, vacation, family and medical leave, and personal time need to be taken into account. A more accurate method of calculating weekly costs might be to divide the annual costs by 48 weeks instead of 52 (to account for time off).

The cancellation rate needs to be factored in, that is, the average or expected number of hours that will not be rendered due to client cancellations.

The final fee of $102.50 may be too high for their area. They can adjust this by decreasing costs, increasing productivity standards, or lowering their expected profit margin.

Price is something that has marketing ramifications as well. (See Chapter 8, Marketing for more details.) This clinic may need to do something about its price if the area is saturated with competition and price is a competitive advantage.

Collections history may indicate that pricing needs to be somewhat higher because only a certain percentage of accounts receivable are collected.

Contractual relations may impose limits on acceptable fees. For example, Medicare has its own rate-setting methodology and will only pay the provider a predefined amount (e.g., the Medicare Physicians Fee Schedule for outpatient services).

By adjusting the above example to reflect the weekly cost based on 48 weeks per year instead of 52, by increasing the productivity standard to 30 billable hours, and by lowering the expected margin to 25%, the following hourly fee results:

	Annually	**Weekly (48)**	**Daily**
Recurring Fixed (e.g., rent)	$30,000.00	$625.00	$125.00
Recurring Variable (e.g., utilities)	13,000.00	270.83	54.17
Direct (e.g., personnel and benefits)	150,000.00	3,125.00	625.00
Indirect (e.g., insurance)	12,000.00	250.00	50.00
Total Costs	*$205,000.00*	*$4,270.83*	*$854.17*

Weekly Productivity	**Hours**
Clinician 1	30
Clinician 2	30
Total	*60*

Profit Margin   25.00%

Breakeven	$71.18
Profit Margin	$17.80
Total Hourly Fee	*$88.98*

By adjusting the basic variables of cost, productivity, and margin, the fee is adjusted.

Fee setting and pricing are important activities and need to have a sound rationale behind them. It is generally not acceptable to phone other area clinics and ask what they are charging, and set your fees based on what others in the community are charging. Fees need to be set based on cost, productivity, and margin, not on what others are charging. Because some payers have fixed or discounted rates, it is important that fees for the aggregate mix of payers (the "case mix") be set at levels that will support business, as discussed in Chapter 2, Service Delivery.

Forms of Ownership

A business can be set up in a variety of ways, referred to as forms of ownership. The form you select is a reflection of the structure, intent, plan, and scope of the entity and needs to be considered carefully. Legal counsel and accounting advice are important in selecting a form of ownership because liability and tax issues are involved. For example, a solo practitioner who is set up as a sole proprietor may leave personal assets exposed in the event of a lawsuit. You may want to discuss the various options for incorporating with an attorney or tax accountant. There are advantages and disadvantages to each form of ownership. While each state may recognize different forms of ownership, here are a few common examples.

> ### A note on price fixing
> It is illegal to collude with other providers to set a price in a way that eliminates competition or harms the consumer in some way. Calling around to find out fees as a way of setting your own, while not best practice, is not necessarily illegal. If you use this information and conspire with those you called to set fees at a certain rate, then this is a problem. The best advice on legal matters comes from an attorney.

Sole Proprietorship. This is a simple form of ownership that is relatively easy and inexpensive to establish. There is no difference between the individual and the business. If a business name is chosen, that name can be registered as a "d/b/a" (doing business as). There is no separate tax on the business, and the sole proprietor reports all business income on his or her personal tax return. In addition, the owner is personally liable for all business debts, and personal assets are exposed in the event of a malpractice suit.

Partnerships. These work like sole proprietorships, except that there is more than one owner. Each owner reports his or her share of the business income, and the personal assets of each owner are exposed in a lawsuit or to cover any business debt.

Corporations. Forming and operating a corporation is more complicated and costly than a sole proprietorship. It may be worth the expense, however, because it limits the owners' personal liability for business debts and court judgments against the business. There are several types of corporations from which to choose.

S-Corporation. This is a corporate entity with no separate corporate tax. Instead, all the income flows through to the owner's tax return and is taxed at the owner's personal rate. The S-Corporation provides a veil of protection to the owner by establishing the business as a separate entity, thus limiting exposure to the business assets and protecting the personal assets of the owner.

Limited Liability Corporation (LLC). This is similar to a S-Corporation because it also provides limited personal liability for business debts and claims. LLCs are more like partnerships or sole proprietorships (depending on how many owners there are) regarding taxes because the owners pay taxes on their shares of the business income on their personal tax returns.

FINANCIAL MANAGEMENT

C-Corporation. This is a corporate entity with a separate corporate tax. The corporation gets taxed on income, and the owners also get taxed on their personal income. The C-Corporation provides a veil of protection, limiting exposure to the assets of the business while protecting the assets of the owner. Fringe benefits can be deducted as business expenses, and business profits can be split among the owners of the corporation, which results in paying a lower overall corporate tax rate.

Limited Partnerships. These are more costly and complicated to establish and run. In a limited partnership, there is usually one person or company, the general partner, who solicits investments from others, called limited partners. The general partner controls the day-to-day operations and is personally liable for business debts of the limited partnership (unless the general partner is a corporation or a LLC). Limited partners have minimal control over daily business decisions or operations and have no personal liability for business debts or claims.

Professional Corporation (PC). In this corporation, owners have no personal liability for malpractice of other owners, but the owners must all belong to the same profession.

Not-for-profit Corporations. These are formed to carry out a charitable, educational, religious, literary, or scientific purpose. Not-for-profits are generally not taxed by federal or state governments on income generated from their related activities because they contribute to society. They generally raise cash through public and private grant funds as well as from contributions from businesses and individual benefactors. Not-for-profit corporations have no owners; income is used to strengthen the corporation and/or for activities to further the corporation's mission.

No one choice is right for every business. The appropriate form of ownership should be chosen based on the individual needs of the business and its owner(s), including –

- expenses involved in establishing and maintaining the chosen business structure.
- the personal exposure to debt, risk, and other business liabilities.
- income tax situation of the owner(s).

Financing
Cash is the life-blood of all businesses. Without cash, operations will grind to a halt and the business will cease to exist. Every business needs a source of cash that is not directly related to revenue generating activities, especially during start-up.

Forms of financing include personal funds or savings, credit cards, bank loans, personal loans (from friends or family), or lines of credit.

A business can look profitable on paper, yet not have enough cash on hand to continue operations. For example, if a business sends out $1,000 in invoices, but collects only $100 after 30 days, there may not be enough money to pay all the bills. This is why a source of reserve cash or line of credit is important.

Access to cash will carry varying expenses, depending on the source. For example, if a business maintains a cash reserve, that money is not used to operate and grow the business, where it could possibly generate a greater return. Conversely, a line of credit at a bank does not incur interest charges unless it is used, at which point interest is paid. Some sources of cash or credit are described below.

Personal savings of the owner. The owner's own cash can be used as needed to cover short-term business cash flow problems. It will probably earn a low rate of interest in a savings account.

Cash reserves in the business. The owner can set aside a sum each period to use as cash reserves. This money is taken out of operations and does not generate more business. When it is used, it only costs the interest that would have otherwise been earned on the deposit.

Line of Credit. Based on the business's financial statements as well as the personal credit of the owner, a bank may issue a line of credit that can be used to cover short-term cash needs. Banks will need collateral, such as a lien on accounts receivable or property. This is generally an inexpensive (lower interest) form of credit.

Factoring. Factoring companies pay you cash for your accounts receivable, minus a financing fee. The factoring company then collects your receivables for themselves. This fee is generally higher than the interest you would pay your bank, but the only necessary collateral is typically the accounts receivable.

Credit cards. Using a personal or business credit card for a short-term cash advance is generally more expensive due to interest rates on most credit cards.

Accounting Basics

To organize, record, summarize, and interpret business transactions properly, accountants adhere to what are known as **Generally Accepted Accounting Principles** (GAAP). When a new area of business emerges, The Financial Accounting Standards Board (FASB) issues additional rules that guide people on how to handle these issues. These are analogous to best practice patterns in SLP.

While the specific rules that govern proper accounting practices are too numerous to cover in this chapter, they can be summarized as follows:

- **Going Concern**. The entity needs to be in operation now and in the foreseeable future.

- **Historical Cost**. Assets are generally reflected in terms of their purchase amount, not their appreciated value.

- **Consistency**. Accounting methods need to be applied consistently during and between periods to give an accurate picture of performance.

- **Objectivity**. Transactions are recorded only when they can be measured in some manner. For example, providing services and then sending an invoice to a client are measurable events that presume payment will be made. However, a verbal indication from a prospective client that he or she will schedule an evaluation in the future cannot be recorded since it is not measurable and no arm's length business transaction has taken place.

- **Full Disclosure**. Everything needs to be explained fully. The complex nature of many financial statements requires that footnotes or appendices be provided to describe any assumptions or accounting methods used.

- **Conservatism**. It is generally better to understate an asset than overstate it.

- **Matching**. Revenue should be matched to expenses incurred to generate that revenue.

- **Cash versus Accrual Accounting**. These are methods of recording transactions based on when expenses are paid and income received versus when they are generated.

Accounting Methods

Cash basis. The cash-basis method of accounting reflects income and expenses when cash changes hands. For example, income is recorded when a deposit is made, not when service has been provided and a bill for services is generated. Expenses are recorded when a check is written, not when expenses have been incurred and an invoice is received. Cash-basis accounting is not typically used in large organizations due to the complexity of their financial situations.

Accrual basis: Accrual-based accounting reflects income and expenses when they are generated. For example, income is recorded for the period in which services were delivered, regardless of when the payment is actually received. Likewise, expenses are recorded during the period in which they were incurred, regardless of when the invoice is paid. This is generally considered to be a more accurate accounting method because it matches the income generated in any period to the expenses incurred in order to generate that income.

The accrual method also reflects depreciation on equipment, accrued payroll, and other items. It is rare that cash-based and accrual-based financial statements for the same organization would look the same for any given period. See the Case Study, **Molly's Private Practice,** for an example of cash versus accrual accounting. Tax returns must be prepared on a cash basis, so tax returns and income statements prepared on an accrual basis don't usually match.

Types of Financial Statements

Balance Sheet. This statement describes the financial position of a business by providing a snapshot of what is owned, what is owed, and net worth on the last day of a reporting period (e.g., monthly, quarterly, annually).

Income Statement. This statement provides information on financial efficiency. It measures performance, not cash flow, and provides a "bottom line" number on how much net income was made or lost. It measures performance over a reporting period (e.g., monthly, quarterly, annually). In a "set" of financial statements for an entity, the measurement date for the balance sheet and last day of the income statement period should be the same.

Statement of Cash Flows. This statement provides information on how much cash came in and went out in any given period. Again, cash is the lifeblood of any business, and this is the report that shows financial liquidity.

Statement of Owner's Equity. This statement illustrates the net worth and changes in net worth between reporting periods.

Summary

Given that the provision of speech-language pathology services is a business endeavor, regardless of the environment in which it is practiced, clinicians need to be aware of basic principles of accounting and finance. Understanding the profit motive, budgets, costs and revenue, forms of ownership, and accounting basics will help clinicians do their part to help their organizations run in a fiscally responsible manner.

FINANCIAL MANAGEMENT

Chapter 4
Standards and Compliance

Every clinician has a legal and ethical obligation to meet compliance requirements and the professional and regulatory standards for his or her profession. While managers and administrators must be able to document and verify compliance with standards, every employee plays a role in meeting specific standards of accreditation for the organization. This provides assurance to payers and consumers that the facility and its services comply with expectations for health, safety, fraudulent practice protections, confidentiality, competence of providers, and quality of services.

Chapter Focus

This chapter examines the influences of compliance rules and standards in speech-language pathology (SLP) business practices. To understand the purposes and benefits derived from the myriad of regulations in health services today, the following topics will be reviewed: **credentialing and accreditation; policies and procedures; corporate compliance; conflicts of interest; risk management; privacy;** and **confidentiality.**

Learning Outcomes

Differentiate voluntary from mandatory accreditation and certification.

Describe the role of organizational policies and procedures.

Define corporate compliance and risk management.

Outline the provisions of the Health Insurance Portability and Accountability Act (HIPAA) that affect SLP practices.

Credentialing

In health care organizations, verification of the provider's credentials is essential. Accrediting agencies require that providers, including contract clinicians, be assessed as "competent" and "qualified" providers, based on the standards set by the organization. Most organizations conduct background checks to ensure the employee has no prior criminal offenses not reported on the application and that education claims are accurate. Additionally, applicants may be asked to provide documentation, such as transcripts, to verify they meet the education requirements and to provide evidence of other training, experience, and certification or licenses. Private practices and small organizations may have to "credential" each clinician individually with insurance providers according to state laws. Terms such as "accreditation," "certification," and "licensure" refer to a similar concept, that is, some entity has conferred recognition to an individual or institution based on meeting established criteria or standards. In the case of speech-language pathologists in health care settings, these terms refer to different types of recognition that come from credentialing organizations and that may be mandatory or voluntary.

Mandatory vs Voluntary Accreditations

Silvia is an ASHA-certified SLP practicing in Virginia. To provide services in a hospital in Maryland, it is *mandatory* that she apply for a state license in Maryland. Because she has expertise and 20-years experience focusing in dysphagia practice, she has *voluntarily* decided to apply to the Clinical Specialty Board in Swallowing to become a Board-Recognized Specialist (ASHA). The skilled nursing facility in which she works has *mandatory* facility accreditation by the state. The facility pays and undergoes periodic audits to receive *voluntary* accreditation by the Joint Commission on Accreditation of Healthcare Organizations. The administrators for the facility are required to ensure its employees have current mandatory licenses and certifications. They believe that the additional voluntary accreditation demonstrates their commitment to quality and adherence to the highest level of standards.

Pathway to the Certificate of Clinical Competence

The Council for Clinical Certification (CFCC) develops standards for earning ASHA's Certificate of Clinical Competence (CCC). The Council on Academic Accreditation in Audiology and Speech-Language Pathology (CAA) ensures that academic programs meet the standards set by the CFCC. The standards for CCC in Speech-Language Pathology include –

- graduating from a **CAA-accredited** graduate program,
- passing the PRAXIS Exam, a specialty subject test in speech-language pathology owned and developed by Educational Testing Services (ETS),
- completing a 36-week Clinical Fellowship (for the SLP Certificate of Clinical Competence).

ASHA **certifies** individuals who meet these requirements. The CCC must be maintained annually by meeting ASHA's requirements for continuing education (effective in 2005) and paying an annual fee.

Graduating from an Accredited Graduate Program

Virtually all graduate students in speech-language pathology (SLP) attend graduate programs that have met standards and are accredited by the Council on Academic Accreditation in Audiology and Speech-Language Pathology (CAA). CAA derives its authority and membership from ASHA but functions autonomously. CAA is recognized by the Council for Higher Education Accreditation (CHEA) and the U.S. Department of Education as the accrediting agency for graduate educational programs that provide entry-level professional preparation with a major emphasis in audiology and/or speech-language pathology.

State Licensure

Almost every state in the U.S. also requires SLPs to hold a **license** or registration. Licensure is a state legal requirement to protect consumers by standardizing the qualifications of providers of certain designated services. Each state has an appointed professional board that develops requirements for licensure (which generally resemble ASHA's certification requirements) and establishes processes for application, fees, continuing education, and renewal. Licensure laws are unique to each state although many areas may overlap. For example, emerging areas of practice (such as performing endoscopy for swallowing or voice assessment) may only be performed in states that do not prohibit the practice. Some states may specifically include or exclude the practice in their law, or the Board may, on request, provide an interpretation of the law regarding a particular procedure. Assume that any state-based regulations will vary widely from one state to another.

The state licensing board has legal jurisdiction over professionals who practice in the state; it may impose sanctions for violations, including censure, suspension, or revocation of the license. A professional who breaks other state laws (e.g., engages in insurance fraud) while practicing may also be reported to the Attorney General for prosecution.

Requirements for Practicing in Schools

SLPs who work in school settings may have somewhat different professional requirements depending on the state in which they live. They may not be required to hold licensure or certification to practice, but they may have to pass a state teacher's exam or meet other state requirements for teacher certification. Health care facilities almost universally require certification and/or licensure to meet insurance payer standards, particularly for federal programs such as Medicare and Medicaid. Depending upon the individual state's requirements, SLP Clinical Fellows may obtain provisional licensure and qualify as providers in health care settings (see Table 4-1).

Voluntary Professional Credentials

Many professions offer additional voluntary credentialing programs so practitioners can demonstrate that they have achieved a higher level of training or have a particular area of specialization. These credentials can serve as a means for career advancement. ASHA has developed a process that allows interested groups to form Specialty Recognition Boards to award recognition in various areas of practice. SLPs who meet the criteria set by a particular specialty recognition board may use the designator "Board-Recognized Specialist." Currently, specialty recognition is available to SLPs in fluency, child language, and swallowing.

The Academy of Neurologic Communication Disorders and Sciences (ANCDS) is an independent organization that offers Board Certification for qualifying SLPs. Individuals who meet their criteria are designated as Board Certified in Neurologic Communication Disorders (BC-NCD) in Adults or Children. Board Certification by ANCDS requires a minimum of a masters degree and CCC in SLP, equivalent of 5

years of full-time experience in neurologic communication disorders, passing a written qualifying examination, and preparing and presenting a case study to the members of the Certification Board related to diagnosis and management of an individual with a neurologic communication disorder.

Table 4-1.
Types of Professional Recognition

Type:	Granted to:	Granted by:
Accreditation	Graduate programs in SLP	CAA
Certification	SLPs who meet requirements	ASHA
Licensure	SLPs who meet requirements	State licensure board
Specialty Recognition	Certified SLPs who meet the requirements	ASHA Boards
Board Certification	SLPs who meet requirements	ANCDS

Code of Ethics

ASHA's Code of Ethics (ASHA, 2003) provides "inspirational and aspirational" guidance for moral behavior as well as statements involving professional conduct or prohibitions to certified SLPs or Clinical Fellows. It includes provisions addressing clinicians' responsibility for the welfare of clients, competence, truthfulness of statements, and professional behavior.

Ethical Practice Requirements

Maintaining your professional certification entails conforming to broad standards of practice in addition to meeting entry-level requirements. Under ASHA's certification, these standards are expressed through a hierarchy of policy documents, including the Scope of Practice for the Profession of Speech-Language Pathology, the Preferred Practice Patterns, and more specific practice policy documents (e.g, position statements, guidelines, knowledge and skills) (ASHA, 2002).

Adherence to the Code of Ethics is a requirement for SLP certification, and it underlies other guidance contained in the practice policy documents. The Scope of Practice, Preferred Practice Patterns, and other policy documents provide guidance to SLPs on their professional practice. These documents are not "cookbooks" or specific requirements for treating certain types of clients. They are based on the most current evidence-based information available and should be used as a framework to develop assessments and treatments. SLPs are also expected to use their clinical judgment, and the clients' individual functional abilities, goals and preferences, and their cultural and linguistic background. (See also the discussion of the importance of ethical practices in Chapter 2, Service Delivery.]

Ethics Violations

Sometimes confusion arises over the correct jurisdiction to address violations of professional standards. ASHA's Code of Ethics applies only to ASHA-certified SLPs and audiologists. Licensure requirements apply to individuals practicing within a particular state who hold a license to practice in that state. Individuals who represent themselves as SLPs without holding a license, for example, should be reported to the state licensure board, since ASHA has no jurisdiction over noncertified SLPs. Illegal acts (such as billing for services that were never rendered) are potential violations of the professional Code of Ethics, state licensure, and state and federal laws. Certified SLPs are bound by the Code of Ethics to report any such violations to the Board of Ethics through ASHA. The Board of Ethics will hear the facts in the case and make a determination as to whether the action is a violation of the Code. The Board can impose sanctions on its members, such as suspension or revocation of the Certificate of Clinical Competence.

Facility Accreditation

All types of health care facilities hold one or more forms of accreditation or certification. Each state certifies or licenses facilities such as hospitals, skilled nursing or long-term care facilities, and home health agencies and performs some form of periodic inspection and review. To be eligible for Medicare reimbursement, facilities must meet Conditions of Participation (COP) that are verified by state survey to certify Medicare eligibility. Some accrediting organizations, such as the Joint Commission on Accreditation of Healthcare Organizations (JCAHO), have been approved to grant Medicare eligibility status to facilities that receive JCAHO accreditation (referred to as "Medicare deemed status"). Other examples of

---

A Clinician's Dilemma

Rick and Kim worked as SLPs in an outpatient clinic. Kim left abruptly and moved to another state. After her departure, Rick's supervisor went through Kim's clients' charts and noticed that she had failed to send monthly summaries to several clients' physicians for the 30-day renewal of orders required by Medicare. The supervisor has asked Rick to write these progress notes and backdate them so they could be sent to the physicians.

Rick doesn't feel comfortable doing this because he knows it is illegal to alter or backdate documentation. In addition, the Code of Ethics mandates against misrepresenting services that were delivered. While Rick's manager could threaten to fire him for not complying, Rick would face a greater risk if he creates fraudulent documentation. Involving the physician in certifying services based on altered documentation could also place the physician in jeopardy.

Rick met with his supervisor to share his concerns. He offered to write a summary note based on available notes from Kim, with the stipulation that he would put the current date on the note, clearly identify the source of the information, the dates of services, who provided the services, and indicate that the note was authored by him for the purpose of a summary.

Rick's manager reluctantly agreed, knowing that the services would probably be denied because Kim had not adhered to the documentation requirements for Medicare coverage. Because Rick was well informed about the law and ethics of his situation, his supervisor could not coerce him into writing fraudulent documentation.

---

accrediting organizations (see Table 4-2) include CARF (CARF–The Rehabilitation Accreditation Commission), and CHAP (Community Health Accreditation Program).

Voluntary accrediting organizations, such as those listed above, offer health care facilities the opportunity to earn accreditation that they may represent as a "quality seal of approval" to the consumer. Accreditation means that the facility has met accrediting organizations' standards based on a rigorous review of documentation and a periodic on-site survey. Failure to earn or maintain accreditation may have a significant impact on a facility's public image, marketing, and financial viability.

Table 4-2.
Voluntary Accrediting Organizations

Joint Commission on Accreditation of Healthcare Organizations (JCAHO) Accredits Hospitals, Ambulatory Care, Long-Term Care and Assisted Living, Home Care, Behavioral Health Care, Networks.
National Committee for Quality Assurance (NCQA): Accredits Managed Care Organizations, Preferred Provider Organizations; develops measures for outcomes.
CARF–The Rehabilitation Accreditation Commission (CARF) Accredits rehabilitation, vocational, and/or mental health programs.
Community Health Accreditation Program (CHAP) Accredits home health agencies.

Policies, Procedures, Qualified Providers, and Competencies

While accrediting standards address a broad range of areas (e.g., provision of care, ethics, leadership, human resources, information management, environment of care), individual clinicians will be most affected by the organization's policies and procedures, the requirements for "qualified providers," and the need to maintain competencies to practice with the population with which they are working (e.g., age range and disorder types).

Policies and Procedures

Agencies will have a policy and procedure manual that describes how operations are expected to be conducted within that facility. SLP units or departments will have "department-specific" or "unit-specific" policies and procedures that have a format and content that is consistent with and complements the organization's policies and procedures. ASHA policy documents can serve as an excellent resource and support for the development of SLP unit-specific policies and procedures. When preparing policies and procedures, it is important to consider that any rules you establish for yourself or your department must be achievable. For example, if your policy states that "staff will check the temperature of the clinic refrigerator where feeding therapy supplies are kept on a DAILY basis to ensure temperatures are maintained within a range of 34-40 degrees F," be sure there are personnel available 7 days a week (weekends and holidays) to follow that policy. (See Appendix H for an Example of a Department-Specific Policy and Procedures.)

Qualified Providers

All SLP staff should have current documentation on file of their certification and/or license, verifying they have the necessary qualifications to practice according to the requirements of the state and the insurance providers (such as Medicare and Medicaid).

Competencies

SLPs should have on file a written set of competencies that identify areas of practice in which they can provide services and the age groups for which they are competent to provide the services. For example, if Carmen was not trained in graduate program to perform modified barium swallows (MBS), a facility or SLP unit would need to demonstrate how she was deemed competent to conduct those studies. They may use ASHA's knowledge and skills statements to develop a list of competencies or to create a simplified version. The purpose of a competency assessment is to evaluate and verify a clinician's mastery of the competencies required for the job through various indictors (continuing education, specialized training, previous experience, etc.). Competency reviews typically indicate the age group(s) for which the individual is competent to serve. Clinicians tend to have experience working with either children or adults; however, they should have competencies to work with both populations if they treat clients of all ages. Clinicians who work with specialized populations (such as children with cochlear implants; AAC, fluency, or tracheotomized/ventilator-dependent patients; and geriatric clients) should maintain documentation of course work, readings, special credentials, special training, or continuing education that

A Manager's Dilemma

LaTonya was updating the clinic's personnel files in April for an anticipated JCAHO survey and asked her staff to provide copies of their current state licenses. Mary came to her with the confession that she realized she had forgotten to send in her licensure renewal, and her license had now expired. She had been seeing patients for two weeks with an expired license.

On receiving this news, LaTonya immediately relieved Mary of all patient care responsibilities because she does not currently hold a state license and cannot legally practice in the state. She instructed Mary to take the necessary steps immediately to reinstate her license. Mary and LaTonya then reviewed the licensure law to identify any renewal "grace period" and to determine the sanctions and remedies that are contained in the statute. LaTonya notified the Human Resources Office and the Risk Manager in her facility about this situation and advised them of the circumstances, applicable sanctions and remedies, and the action plans. LaTonya and Mary followed the counsel of the Risk Manager. As part of the corrective action plan, LaTonya will credit all services provided while Mary was not licensed and will ensure there is effective, ongoing monitoring to prevent any future lapses in license renewals.

contributed to their competency with a specific group of clients. (See Appendix I, Staff Competency Assessment for an example of an assessment for an AAC specialty in pediatric practice.)

Corporate Compliance

The phrase "corporate compliance" refers specifically to formal programs and practices within health care organizations that developed in response to the Stark Laws and Medicare Fraud and Abuse protection requirements. These protections essentially ensure that physicians do not engage in self-referral or "kickback" practices that would result in illegal charges to Medicare.

Self-Referral is when a physician refers to an entity with which the physician or a member of the physician's family has a financial relationship. The relationship is such that the physician would earn a financial return based on the success of a clinic in which he or she has a financial interest. The Stark II Law designates ten categories of Medicare and Medicaid health services for which self-referral is prohibited. Speech-language pathology services, durable medical equipment, orthotics, and prosthetics are included as designated health services.

Kickbacks are anything of value presented to a practitioner or supplier that may induce that entity to offer referrals. Corporate compliance programs ensure that all officers, managers, and employees in a health care organization meet any governmental (federal, state, or local) statutes, contractual and legal obligations, or professional ethical practice requirements.

Facilities typically have a compliance office, with staff overseen by a compliance officer, usually a physician or an attorney. The compliance office tracks state and federal regulations, particularly Medicare rules, guidelines, and statutes, to keep practitioners apprised of any changes affecting them. The compliance office ensures that procedures are accurately coded, in accordance with CPT descriptors and ICD-9 codes (see Chapter 2, Service Delivery) and that documentation aligns with the charges billed through oversight processes such as audits. For example, if a bill was generated for a modified barium swallow study by the SLP on a given date of service and there was no supportive documentation to indicate the client was seen on that date, the compliance office could request corrective actions be taken (refunding the payment for the unsupported charge). The compliance office seeks to prevent and avoid penalties from Medicare for coding and billing errors. The compliance office may also determine the mandatory compliances expected from each employee to allow the organization to maintain its accreditation. Examples of mandatory annual compliances include confidentiality training, conflict of interest assurances, and policy reviews, as well as annual TB tests, fire safety, and infection control training.

Conflict of Interest

The need to recognize potential conflicts of interest in health care services and research is increasingly emphasized in the workplace. Employees usually must complete a form annually that itemizes potential conflicts for scrutiny by the compliance office. If you provide consultation for or represent a vendor or other entity and are in a position to give them an advantage of some sort in negotiations with your facility, you must withdraw from any role in the decision making. This applies to purchasing, contracts, or any other dealings your facility might have with the company.

Similarly, researchers, in their presentations and publications, must prominently identify any relationship they have with a vendor or funding group and make others aware of conflicts of interest when presenting their research findings to ensure that potential biases are not hidden.

Risk Management

Risk management refers to the prevention and protection processes, policies, and procedures that are in place to minimize risk. These include –

- risks to the health and safety of clients and employees (e.g., employee health protections, adherence to environment of client care standards),
- risks for legal actions (e.g., ensuring orders are properly entered, dated, and signed),
- risks to the financial viability of the organization or agency (e.g., ensuring payment is authorized prior to providing services).

Risk management, along with compliance, ensures proper policies and procedures are in place and followed to reduce any risks of harm (physical, legal, financial) to individuals or to the organization.

Health Insurance Portability and Accountability Act (HIPAA)

Every health care practitioner, including speech-language pathologists, should now be well aware of the administrative and confidentiality requirements of the HIPAA statute. (Also see Appendix J, A Look at Privacy and Confidentiality.) The three regulations HIPAA implemented include –

- **privacy of protected health information (PHI)**, (April 2003)
- **transaction - electronic data interchange**, (October 2003)
- **security of the data**. (April 2005)

These regulations apply to insurance entities, research data, and any aspect of health care services that involves the transmission of any health related information in an electronic form or any "clearinghouse" situation or database involving protected health information. The law also applies to business associates who handle protected information on behalf of the covered entity. For covered entities, all health care information, regardless of whether it is maintained in electronic form or paper records, is covered by HIPAA, as is the transmission of information orally, in writing, or by fax. The law does not prohibit health care providers from disclosing a client's personal health care information for the purposes of treatment, payment for services, and health care operations. Whether SLPs work in a hospital or rehab agency or work for a contract agency that supplies providers to a health care setting, they must adhere to HIPAA regulations and the privacy policies of their employer. Health care facilities are also required to maintain written business agreements with their business associates to verify their knowledge and compliance with HIPAA regulations.

Privacy

Although ASHA's Code of Ethics (Principle I, Rule L) addresses the importance of maintaining confidentiality, HIPAA makes this expectation a legal requirement. HIPAA, a federal law, is the basis of privacy regulation unless exceeded by state laws that are more stringent. Violations of a client's privacy can result in penalties including fines and even prison sentences.

Clients' protected health information includes name, Social Security number, financial data, medical record number, and all other identifying information and the contents of their medical records.

Health care facilities must demonstrate compliance in the following areas:

- Develop policies and procedures manuals that describe how they are complying with HIPAA.
- Distribute a "Notice of Privacy Practices" to clients that describes their rights regarding their protected information.
- Obtain written client authorization for the release of their protected health information for purposes other than treatment, payment, and health care operations.
- Document that employees have been trained on policies and procedures.
- Maintain written agreements with business associates to assure their compliance with HIPAA regulations.

To comply with HIPAA, facilities have made changes such as –

- modifying waiting areas to afford privacy for communication with the client.

- eliminating information about the client's condition that can be viewed by the public (e.g., detailed sign-in sheets, signs at the patient's bedside).
- keeping medical records (including the SLPs' "soft charts") locked and secured to prevent access.
- putting fax machines in areas that do not have public access.
- placing privacy warnings on fax and e-mail communications.

Clients' Privacy Rights

Clients have the right to know that their protected information will not be disclosed without their permission unless explicitly allowed by the privacy rule. They have the right to –

- receive a copy of the "Notice of Privacy Policies,"
- request that the release of their protected information be restricted to specific individuals,
- know who has had access to their information,
- read and amend their records if they feel information is missing or inaccurate,
- file a complaint with the Health and Human Services Office of Civil Rights if they believe their rights have been violated.

Security

The security rule specifies a series of administrative, technical, and physical security procedures for covered entities to use to protect electronic protected health information in its custody from potential security threats and hazards. The standards are delineated into either required or addressable implementation specifications. Covered providers are required to document their security procedures as well as document any undertaken risk analysis to support their implementation decisions.

Electronic Data Interchange (EDI)

The EDI regulation mandates that covered entities use a specific technical standard for transmitting electronic data. Standardizing formats for each type of transmission increases the accessibility of information and decreases overhead costs otherwise needed to receive and convert data from other entities. Types of electronic transmissions covered by HIPAA include –

- health care claims,
- claims status and remittance advices,
- eligibility verifications and responses,

- referrals and authorizations,
- coordination of benefits.

Larger health care entities have upgraded their software to comply with EDI standards. Smaller practices may choose to file their claims through clearinghouses that reformat the data according to EDI standards and transmit to the payer. Or entities can subscribe to an application service provider (ASP), which provides the necessary software for the provider to submit claims.

Summary

Every employee in a health care service setting must meet all applicable legal, regulatory, and ethical standards; protect confidentiality; and achieve and maintain the dictates of the risk management and corporate compliance offices. To compound this challenge, the standards require constant attention and adjustment due to –

- periodic changes in professional requirements (e.g., changes in certification standards);
- annual changes in accreditation standards (e.g., JCAHO);
- changes in federal regulations (e.g., new requirements for supervision of students; limits on size of groups under Medicare's Prospective Payment System);
- new legislation (e.g., HIPAA, Stark Laws);
- changes in state regulations (e.g., requiring continuing education hours to maintain licensure, changing provider qualifications for Medicaid).

References

American Speech-Language-Hearing Association. (2002). *ASHA Desk Reference 2002.* Rockville, MD: Author.

American Speech-Language-Hearing Association. (2003). Code of ethics (rev.). *ASHA Supplement 23*, 13-15.

Chapter 5
Quality and Performance Improvement

There are many aspects of clinical services that contribute to quality care. Speech-language pathologists (SLPs) should be aware that merely meeting ASHA standards, state licensing standards, or the standards of accrediting groups does not guarantee quality services. Quality has multidimensional characteristics and is defined by many different constituents. Quality is a "moving target." To achieve and maintain quality, there has to be a continuous emphasis on performance improvement and a diligent effort to be better than "just good enough."

Quality is the extent to which products or services meet or exceed expectations. In service organizations, high quality is synonymous with excellence. Quality processes or procedures in health care increase the likelihood of desired health outcomes, increase customer satisfaction, and ultimately ensure the financial well-being of the organization.

Performance improvement (PI) is the continuous study and adaptation of a health care organization's functions and processes to increase the probability of achieving desired outcomes and to better meet the needs of clients and other users of services. PI is a philosophy that encourages every member of an organization to aspire to the achievement and maintenance of quality. Therefore, quality and performance improvement are closely linked.

Chapter Focus

This chapter explores the various sides of quality. We will describe methods for achieving quality and the importance of quality to the

Learning Outcomes

List the characteristics of a high quality health care organization.

Discuss the inter-relationship between quality and performance improvement.

Describe the importance of continuous performance improvement in achieving and maintaining quality services and a competitive advantage.

List the steps of the performance improvement process.

Describe the method and importance of benchmarking.

customers, employees, other stakeholders, and to the organization as a whole. Although a minimum level of acceptable quality can be obtained, performance can always be improved. Therefore, continuous performance improvement is discussed as a method to achieve and maintain an above average level of care. In this chapter, the importance of the **quality of services** and **continuous performance improvement programs** are emphasized, not only for the sake of the customers, but also for the financial viability of the organization.

Quality

Quality is something that occurs when an organization strives to achieve customer satisfaction and loyalty by exceeding their expectations. Going beyond normal expectations is what makes an organization or program recognized for its quality. In health care, quality includes –

- the best possible clinical outcomes for clients,
- customer (internal and external) satisfaction,
- employee satisfaction and retention,
- sound financial performance (Leebov, 1991).

Quality is usually defined by the customers' perception of a variety of factors. Since the perception of quality is important, the organization should not only strive to achieve and continually improve quality, but also ascertain if there is agreement about what quality means to its customers, employees, competitors, and the community-at-large. External customers include clients and their families, insurance companies, state and federal regulatory agencies, and referring agencies. Internal customers include coworkers, managers, and owners.

Quality organizations are recognized among their peers for providing high quality care. In general, clients using speech-language pathology services want the following from a high quality health care organization (Davis, Aquilano, & Chase, 1999):

- Consistency and dependability. Clients expect clinicians to be prepared for each session.
- Responsiveness of employees to questions and concerns (from the intake clerk arranging the first visit, to the SLP seeing the client, to the account office staff managing the billing).
- Competence. Clients expect the SLP to have the appropriate training and demonstrated competencies to provide age-appropriate service. All individuals in the organization are expected to be competent, including administrators and managers.
- Respectful and considerate treatment.

- Ethical treatment. Clients expect individuals in the organization to be credible, trustworthy, and reliable.
- Safety. Clients expect to be free from risks of physical danger. They also expect that decisions about clinical management are appropriate and in their best interests.
- Accessibility. Clients expect the organization to make it easy to speak with someone who will listen.
- Information. Clients expect to be informed.
- Understanding. Clients expect others to respond to their individual needs and wishes.

Ensuring Quality

Leaders of an organization have significant influence over the quality process and ensuring quality outcomes. They are responsible for planning and directing the activities of the organization (see Chapter 1, Leadership) and have the opportunity to control many of the variables that affect what is done, when it is done, who does it, and how well it is done. Although the decisions and actions of the leaders have a great effect on the achievement of quality, all members of an organization, including speech-language pathologists and support staff, have the responsibility to ensure quality. Everyone has a responsibility to help the organization make changes if necessary to achieve and maintain quality services.

In speech-language pathology, a number of factors affect the perception of quality:

- Reputation of the program.
- Experience, skill, and competence of the clinical staff.
- Consistency and dependability of services.
- Wait time for appointments.
- Referral rates.
- Friendliness and attitude of the staff.
- Accessibility of services.
- Cleanliness and appearance of clinic.
- Professional appearance of the staff.
- Staff's responsiveness to clients' needs.
- Staff longevity.
- Financial performance of the program.

How can SLP clinicians ensure quality?

- Focus on the primary customers (clients and families) and determine what they hope to achieve through the services.
- Attend to the needs of all other customers (physicians, coworkers, etc.).
- Strive to exceed the customers' expectations for quality, outcomes, timeliness, efficiency, and friendliness.
- Correct problems affecting the quality of services.
- Seek opportunities for continuous improvement.
- Provide services that adhere to all professional standards.
- Understand and comply with the organization's mission, vision, and values.
- Take responsibility for professional development and continuous learning.
- Participate in performance improvement teams and activities.

How can managers ensure quality?

- Understand the internal and external customer needs.
- Ensure all service providers have the training, knowledge, skills, competencies, and resources they need to do a good job.
- Ensure all staff meet the organization's standards.
- Ensure that the organization has the right structure, the right processes, and the right people for the job.
- Charter and lead performance improvement teams.

How can leaders ensure quality?

- Foster an organizational commitment to quality.
- Demand everyone be "customer focused."
- Plan strategically so that the organization can fulfill its mission, vision, and values.
- Empower employees to initiate problem solving.
- Align systems within the organization so everyone works together (Covey, 1989).

Malcolm Baldrige National Quality Award

The importance of quality in organizations is formally recognized by our federal government through the annual Malcolm Baldrige National Quality Award. Established in 1987, this award promotes quality awareness, establishes guidelines and criteria for quality, recognizes quality achievements, and publicizes successful quality strategies. The Criteria for Performance Excellence are built upon a set of inter-related core values, which describe beliefs and behaviors that are embedded in high-performing organizations. The criteria include –

- leadership,
- strategic planning,
- customer and market focus,
- measurement, analysis, and knowledge management,
- human resource focus,
- process management,
- business results.

Speech-language pathologists who are in leadership positions can use these criteria to determine if an organization is providing quality care and is a good place to work.

Let's consider some of the characteristics of high quality organizations.

Customer-Driven Excellence

Leaders of quality organizations realize that customers play a large role in defining quality and that customer satisfaction leads to customer loyalty. Customer-driven excellence involves –

- understanding the desires of today's customers and anticipating the desires of future customers and marketplaces.
- reducing errors and eliminating causes of customer dissatisfaction.
- providing the basic services that the customer desires and services that distinguish the organization from the competition.
- anticipating changes in the marketplace.

Organizational and Employee Motivation, Learning, and Satisfaction

Organizations that continuously encourage learning at all levels should demonstrate enhanced performance. Employees who are engaged in personal learning experiences report higher job satisfaction. Personal learning can make the organization more innovative. Learning should be –

- a daily activity,
- practiced at all levels of the organization,
- utilized for organizational and personal problem solving,
- cooperative,
- used to encourage employees to make a contribution to the organization,

Visionary Leadership

Creates customer focus, clear and visible values, and high expectations (which balance the need of all stakeholders).

Ensures the creation of strategies, systems, and methods for achieving excellence, while stimulating innovation and building knowledge and capabilities.

Inspires and motivates the workforce to contribute, develop, learn, and to be innovative and creative.

Serves as a role model by reinforcing ethics, vision, actions, and performance.

Provides a climate for both personal (within employees) and organization learning.

- motivational,
- rewarded.

Valuing Employees and Partners

Health care organizations have both internal and external partners. Employees are internal partners. Examples of external partners include universities, professional associations, and educational groups. High quality companies nurture these relationships, which are also important in advocacy (see Chapter 9, Advocacy). High quality health care organizations value external partners by –

- regular communication,
- regular feedback and evaluation,
- mutual strategic planning.

Agility

A high quality health care organization has the capacity for rapid change and flexibility. As the marketplace changes, agile organizations are able to make the necessary work process changes to remain competitive.

Focus on the Future

High quality health care organizations understand the short-term as well as the long-term factors that impact the organization's ultimate success. They plan for the future by attending to –

- customer expectations,
- new business and partnering opportunities,
- technological development,
- evolving regulatory requirements,
- community and social expectations.

Managing for Innovation

High quality health care organizations know that innovation results in meaningful changes to services and processes, thus creating new value. Innovation is part of the culture of quality organizations.

Managing by Facts

High quality organizations use many sources of data and information to –

- analyze overall performance,
- improve operations,
- make management changes,

- compare performance with competitors (e.g., "best practices" or performance benchmarks, see Chapter 2, Service Delivery).

Social Responsibility

Leaders of high quality health care organizations acknowledge the organization's responsibility to –

- behave ethically throughout the organization and in all transactions,
- protect the public,
- influence others to demonstrate social responsibility.

Focus on Results and Value

If a health care organization focuses on results, it can balance the demands of all of its customers, stakeholders, and partners. By also focusing on providing a service or product of value, high quality organizations build loyalty, and establish a sound reputation.

Systems Perspective

Organizations that successfully manage overall performance are able to –

- **synthesize** – ensure strategic objectives and action plans are fused within the whole organization.
- **align actions** – ensure plans, processes, measures, and actions are consistent.
- **integrate** – ensure components of systems are interconnected.

Performance Improvement

In the early 1980s, health care organizations were required to engage in quality assurance (QA) activities to meet accreditation standards. QA activities were primarily reactions to problems, rather than systemic, proactive programs. Today, leaders realize that systematic, ongoing attention to quality, or continuous quality improvement (CQI), is essential for accreditation. It has also proven to be an effective business strategy because it focuses on an ongoing effort to improve quality. CQI is essential to achieve and maintain the financial well-being of an organization.

In order to monitor, maintain, and improve quality, health care organizations typically have a performance improvement (PI) program, which is a way to achieve continuous quality improvement. Performance improvement is the continuous and ongoing study and adaptation of an organization's processes and functions to increase the probability of achieving desired outcomes. In health care, PI programs seek not only to reduce risks of harm or injury to clients, but also to better meet

Quality Assurance	Continuous Quality Improvement
Examines	Seeks
Reactive	Proactive
Corrects (fixes symptoms)	Prevents (fixes causes)
Involves a few members of the organization	Involves all members of the organization
Emphasizes numbers and standards	Emphasizes methods and processes
Seeks to achieve standards	Seeks to exceed standards

the needs of clients, families, and other customers. A PI program is based on the assertion that performance can always be improved, even if it's already at a high level. It involves actively searching for opportunities for improvement and looking for new and better ways of doing things. The purpose of PI programs is to improve the quality, safety, efficiency, and cost-effectiveness of client care.

Although the leaders of the organization are usually responsible for the development, approval, and implementation of the PI program, the best ideas for improvements come from people who actually do the work. A PI program should involve everyone in the organization at every level. In many cases, performance improvement activities are planned and implemented by teams of people who have knowledge about the particular aspect of the care that is the focus of improvement.

In health care, organizations that seek accreditation by the Joint Commission for Accreditation of Healthcare Organizations (JCAHO) are required to implement a PI program. Leaders in organizations strive to achieve excellence not simply to meet accrediting standards but to provide the best possible care for their clients. Equally importantly, they also achieve a competitive advantage over others. Organizations that are viewed as providing excellent services have an advantage in staff recruitment and retention.

A performance improvement program in speech–language pathology should be designed to ensure that services are of high quality, consistent with the standards of care set by the profession, and reflect the organization's mission, vision, values, and strategic plan (see Chapter 1, Leadership). The program should make sure that all services meet or exceed the customers' expectations of quality. The program should evaluate and monitor the quality of all important aspects of clinical care, particularly those that are high volume, high risk, or problem prone.

In speech-language pathology, as in other health care disciplines, there are many aspects of care that could be monitored and evaluated for opportunities to improve. The JCAHO lists the following areas for consideration in providing health care:

- **Efficacy**—the care of the client has been shown to accomplish the desired or projected outcome(s).
- **Appropriateness**—the care is relevant to the client's clinical needs, given the current state of knowledge.

- **Availability**—appropriate care is available to meet the client's needs.
- **Timeliness**—the care is provided to the client at the most beneficial or necessary time.
- **Effectiveness**—the care is provided in the correct manner, given the current state of knowledge, to achieve the desired or projected outcome for the client.
- **Continuity**—the care for the client is coordinated among practitioners, among organizations, and over time.
- **Safety**—the risk of an intervention or risk in the environment of care is reduced for the client and others, including the health care provider.
- **Efficiency**—the outcomes of care are balanced against the resources required to deliver it.
- **Respect and caring**—the client (or family member) is involved in care decisions, and those providing services show sensitivity and respect for the client's needs, expectations, and individual differences.

Quality in Strategic Planning

Evaluating quality and performance is particularly important when developing a strategic plan, establishing new services, processes or programs, or redesigning current ones. As part of the strategic planning process, the following questions should be asked:

- Is the new procedure, process, function, or service consistent with the organization's mission, vision, values, and plans?
- What will our clients, staff, and other customers expect from the process, function, or service? How do they think it will work? What results do they anticipate?
- What have scientific and professional experts and other reliable sources said about the new procedure, process, function, or service?
- What information is available about the performance of similar processes, functions, or services in other organizations?

Examples of strategic planning goals include improving –

- access and efficiencies,
- transitions in care services across a continuum,
- safety,
- clinical quality and outcomes,
- staff competence,

- communications,
- profitability.

Process and Tools

Health care organizations might choose to use performance improvement teams to solve urgent problems, make continual improvements, reduce the risk for problems, or prevent the reoccurrence of problems. These work teams are composed typically of clinical, support, and management members who meet regularly to monitor and identify processes potentially affecting the quality of care. They investigate the causes of problems, recommend solutions, and take corrective actions. There are several types of performance improvement teams. Roles, responsibilities, tasks, and composition vary in format. Teams that focus more internally may be referred to as operational teams. Teams that focus more on organizational systems may be referred to as systems teams. Teams that are future-focused may be referred to as strategy teams.

There are several models for implementation of a PI program that performance improvement teams might use. One commonly applied approach is the Plan-Do-Check-Act (PDCA) Cycle (JCAHO, 2004), also referred to as the Plan-Do-Study-Act (PDSA) Cycle (JCAHO, 2000). These methods originated with Walter Stewhart and were later applied by Deming as methods for understanding process variations in quality control (JCAHO, 2000). Using the four major components of the model, the development and implementation of a performance improvement program are described below.

Plan

- Opportunities for improvement of client care are identified. This can be done by brainstorming, where a group of people freely list ideas that come to mind.
- A plan is developed to improve an aspect of client care or service delivery.
- The current process or procedure is analyzed, and a plan for improvement is developed.
- Specific indicators of quality and performance are identified to monitor and evaluate those aspects of client care. An indicator is a measure used to determine performance of certain processes or functions and the ultimate outcomes.
- The data source, method of collection, sampling size, and time frame are identified for each indicator.

Do

- The plan is implemented.
- Data are collected and documented.

Check

- The results are examined to determine how effective the plan was.

- If the data suggest a persistent or new problem, the problem is further evaluated through a root cause analysis. A root cause analysis (RCA) refers to an attempt to search for and evaluate causal factors related to adverse outcomes or events. In addition, proactive analysis of high-risk processes is also required by JCAHO standards. Risk assessment, or failure modes and effect analysis (FMEA), involves identifying potential breakdowns in a process and determining why they could occur, then implementing and monitoring a redesigned process.

- The probable causes and contributing factors are determined.

- Possible solutions and opportunities for improvement are identified.

- A plan for action is developed and documented. All decision making at this point is data-driven.

Act

- The plan is implemented to correct or improve the problem areas.

- A follow-up assessment is done to determine whether improvement has occurred as a result of the plan's implementation. If not, changes are made to the plan or another plan is developed, documented, implemented, and evaluated.

- The results of performance improvement projects are documented and shared with all staff members in the organization.

Tools for Performance Improvement

CQI teams sometimes find it is useful to "chart" out or systematically analyze the relationship between various process elements that are contributing to a problem and to track trends and results by using illustrative tools or graphic methods for presenting data. These tools are described in books and publications by JCAHO. There are also a number of vendors who provide downloadable software for use by managers, which can transition your data tables into graphs by making the calculations and providing a variety of charts and tools. To understand better how some of these tools are applied, it may be helpful to look at an example.

Annie is a manager of SLP services in "Origami Rehab Inc. (ORI)." ORI was considering moving from a largely paper system for client records to an entirely electronic (e-chart) system, mainly because they have a problem getting information requested by third-party payers to them in a timely manner. The cost for equipment and training for e-chart are important considerations, but if fewer processing steps and quicker responses to third-party payer requests for documentation could be achieved, then the investment would be worthwhile. Annie's CQI team used tools to help track, analyze, support, and evaluate the transition to e-charts.

The Team initially examined the work flow for third-party billing processing (see Figure 5-1, Flow Chart), and found queries were stalled whenever the insurance clerk did not have all the information he needed to make decisions, abstract data from the medical record, and then send the requested information to Patient Accounting for submission to the payers. A Pareto diagram (see Figure 5-2) provided the team with a means to look at the sources of all processing delays and the extent to which each source contributed to the overall problem. The greatest contributor (highest percentage) of the source for delays was due to a single factor: clinician tardiness in providing the requested information. This supported the decision to implement electronic data retrieval with an e-chart, as it would almost entirely eliminate the need to contact a clinician to obtain visit data.

Figure 5-1.
Flow Chart: Retrieval of Visit Data From Medical Record to Substantiate Charges to Third-Party Payer

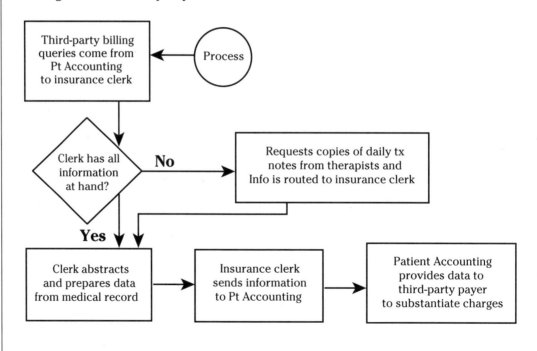

Prior to and after the e-chart training was introduced, a histogram (see Figure 5-3) helped the team to demonstrate the resulting changes in the volume of paper versus electronic records managed by the insurance clerk across four quarters. This chart illustrated how, after the e-chart training implementation, there was almost a complete elimination of paper record abstracting and also an increase in the number of records processed.

Figure 5-2.
Pareto Diagram: Examination of Sources for Delays in Retrieving Visit Data

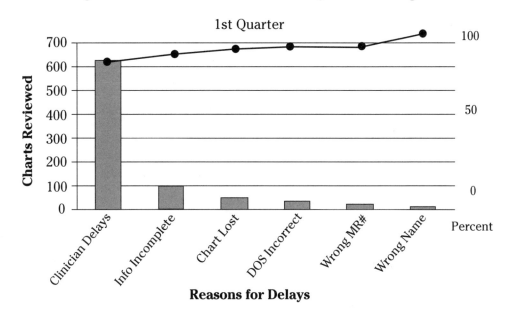

To further examine the question of the cost-benefit of investing in the equipment and training needed for e-chart access, a control chart (Figure 5-4) provided a display of the average days required to process (retrieve and send) requested data. The control chart's "upper control limit" for processing requests was 50 days, which was well outside of a target of no more than 10 business days for response time. This excessive delay meant that requested information would often be processed too late for payment. The average delays dramatically decreased over four quarters, once e-charts were fully implemented. Response times met the 10-day delay target at the 27th week and nearly reached a "lower control limit" of a 1-day turn-around by the last half of the last quarter.

Flow charts. A flow chart is a pictorial representation of the steps and sequence of steps within a process. Flow charts allow us to examine how steps in a process relate to each other, where decisions are made, and where data are needed to

Figure 5-3.
Histogram: Number of Paper vs Electronic Records Reviewed to Obtain Data Required by Third-Party Payers Across Four Quarters (staff and insurance clerks trained to use electronic medical records in the 2nd quarter)

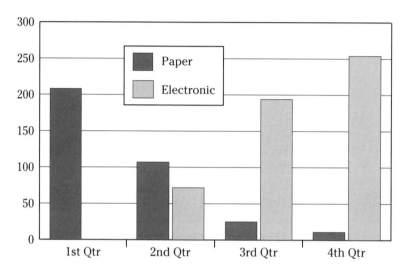

progress to the next step. There are conventional "box" symbols in flow charts; for example, the title of the "process" under examination is usually stated at the top within a circle; each step in the process is then stated within a box or rectangle. A "Yes-No" decision step is presented within a diamond shape. Steps in the process that require data are displayed within parallelograms, and the flow of all of the steps is shown by arrows connecting steps. Flow charts are sometimes used to display Story Boards. Story Boards are merely poster-type displays of the story of the process improvement. Flow charts are one way to illustrate that story by mapping the multiple-steps within a process.

Pareto diagrams. A Pareto diagram is used for comparing measurement results in order to identify major causes of a problem. A vertical bar graph is used to display the relative importance of each contributing cause (such as source of delays, in our example) and the percent of contribution of each cause to the problem (e.g., delays in responding to third-party requests). Pareto charts refer to the "Pareto Principle," which states that only a few factors are responsible for producing most of the problems. This principle can be applied to quality improvement to the extent that a great majority of problems (80%) are produced by a few key causes (20%). If we correct these few key causes, we will have a greater probability of success. In our example, the Pareto chart demonstrates that only one of the major causes of delays (clinician response delays) contributed to nearly 90% of the problem, so a correction that eliminates clinicians from the information retrieval process might virtually eliminate the problem, which was the case.

Histograms. A histogram is a bar graph that displays the distribution of data according to category, graphing the frequency of different events or measurements. The histogram is useful for revealing variation within a process and for displaying results brought about by an implemented change. In this way, it differs from a Pareto diagram, which looks at characteristics of a product or service. A histogram, for example, may be a method of displaying the responses to a consumer satisfaction survey and noting trends.

Figure 5-4.
Control Chart: Average Days Required to Process Request for Medical Records During Transition from Paper to Electronic Data Retrieval Systems

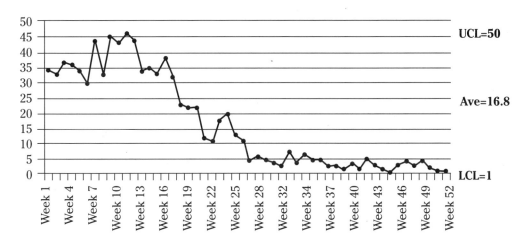

Cause and Effect Diagrams. The cause and effect diagram, also known as the fishbone diagram, is used to collect ideas about possible causes of a problem. The problem (effect) is listed on the right, and possible causes are listed on the limbs and branches that lead to it. Brainstorming is the technique used with this tool. Someone starts by stating what he/she thinks is a possible cause of the problem, and each team member takes a turn. This continues until all ideas about possible causes have been exhausted and are listed on the diagram. It is helpful to categorize causes by labeling the limbs of the diagram and drawing branches from each limb.

Scatter Diagrams. A scatter diagram is used to study relationships between variables and to examine for possible cause and effect relationships, though it is merely illustrative and cannot prove causation. Rather, it can clarify whether a

QUALITY/PERFORMANCE IMPROVEMENT

relationship exists and measure the strength of that relationship. Scatter diagrams display the intersection, correlation, or effect, of one variable when changed upon another variable for the purpose of testing the hypothesis that the two variables are related.

Control Charts. A control chart is used to monitor work processes to detect nonrandom variability patterns based on the concepts of statistical control. It helps to distinguish variability in a process due to unique events/upper and lower control limits. Statistical process control methodology detects whether a process is predictable and capable of meeting requirements.

Benchmarking

Effective leaders realize that performance improvement can be enhanced by working with others outside the organization to develop best practices, those practices that lead to superior performance. Benchmarking is the process by which organizations search for the best practices in other organizations. As part of this process, leaders collaborate with local, state, national, and even international organizations to compare practices in order to find those that lead to the best (greatest quality, most efficient, most cost-effective) outcomes (also see Chapter 2, Service Delivery). By examining the experience of others or participating in databases that provide a comparison of the range of costs and outcomes in other organizations (e.g., ASHA NOMS), leaders can compare their own program's performance to other programs. Leaders can also benchmark to professional standards or reports from other organizations involved in similar practices or to practices in other industries to look for novel and effective models and practices that they can emulate. Benchmarking helps leaders learn from the successes of others and compare their performance to their cohorts.

Summary

Placing a high priority on quality is good for clients and for the provider organizations. Quality is an attribute that is multifactorial, and achieving quality requires involvement and commitment from everyone in the organization. We all want to provide quality services to our clients and their families; however, "good enough" is all too often not good enough when competitors are striving to do better. Competitive leaders have infused concepts for quality into all aspects of the fabric of their organization. The organization's PI program and commitment to CQI are ways to ensure quality is at the forefront of service provision and planning.

Continuous quality improvement gives the organization a competitive edge; it is more cost-effective than the old notions of "quality assurance." CQI seeks to improve processes that will prevent problems, rather than responding to them haphazardly. Prevention is the most cost-effective way to ensure quality services.

References

Covey, S. (1989). *The seven habits of highly effective people*. New York: Free Press/Simon & Schuster.

Davis, M. M., Aquilano, N. J., & Chase, R. B. (1999). *Fundamentals of operations management*. New York: McGraw-Hill/College.

Joint Commission on Accreditation of Healthcare Organizations. (2000). *Using performance improvement tools in health care settings* (rev.ed.). Oakbrook Terrace, IL: Author.

Joint Commission for the Accreditation of Healthcare Organizations (2004). 2004 *Comprehensive accreditation manual for hospitals: The official handbook (CAMH)*. Oakbrook Terrace, IL: Author.

Leebov, W. (1991). *The quality quest: A briefing for health care professionals*. Chicago: American Hospital Publishing.

QUALITY/PERFORMANCE IMPROVEMENT

Chapter 6
Technology

Technology has different meanings to different people. Some consider it the practical application of knowledge to a specific area, such as educational or medical technology. Many people think of technology as the development of products that make our lives easier or better, such as the microwave or CT scan. Others consider technology a process, such as using the computer to do a job more efficiently (e.g., writing clinical reports, tracking outcome data). However we define technology, it can streamline our personal and professional lives.

Chapter Focus
This chapter provides a basic understanding of the **technology tools** available and how they may be used in the clinical setting for documentation, communications and clinical treatments. By understanding what is available and how to use it (or how not to use it), we can improve the quality, accuracy, cost-effectiveness, efficiency, and speed of our work. For clinicians, this can reduce the time usually spent on documentation; for supervisors and administrators, it can result in improved functioning and productivity in a department.

The Human Element
Productivity tools are ubiquitous nowadays; there is a gadget, machine, or piece of software for just about any application. The trick is to find the proper balance of technology and gadgetry for what needs to be done. Using technology just for the sake of using it is often counterproductive. Busy professionals need to use technology in a way that will increase their productivity while improving the quality and accuracy of their services.

Learning Outcomes
Describe considerations for using technology in clinical documentation.

Discuss technology used in diagnoses and treatment.

Describe telepractice and its possible applications and limitations.

Identify how technology can be used for staff development.

List ten considerations for practice automation.

TECHNOLOGY

Not long ago, the only option for clinicians was to document their clinical work using pen and paper. When managing a caseload of 40 or more clients, the limitations quickly become evident. Even the simplest of technological tools, such as word processing software, can make an impact on the way a clinician works by eliminating many repetitive steps in the documentation process. Consider how many times the client's name appears on a document, or how many times you write the same goal, or slightly different versions of the same goal. A simple copy and paste saves a great deal of time over the course of charting for a full caseload. The legibility and storability of the documentation are added advantages.

Many people become overwhelmed or intimidated by all the technological options that are available. It's not necessary to use every bit of technology out there, but it is helpful to identify some high frequency tasks that could be simplified through electronic methods.

Most devices and applications are designed so that the user can learn most of the important functions by simply jumping in and exploring. One good way to avert a technophobic response to a new device or application is to spend a few uninterrupted minutes exploring the features and functions. Once you gain a basic level of comfort with whatever it is you are exploring, you'll start to discover what it has to offer you.

Clinical Documentation

Clinical documentation is necessary for many reasons, including –

- planning treatment,
- tracking progress,
- collaborating and sharing information with other professionals,
- explaining what was accomplished during a visit.

Selecting a technological solution for clinical documentation largely depends on the work setting and the requirements and uses of documentation. For example, solo practitioners may feel that a handwritten record will suffice. This may not be the case in a hospital setting, where a documentation system may be in place already. If you are in the position to create, design, or implement a documentation system, start by reviewing the requirements of the documentation you generate as well as the work flow. There are several off-the-shelf applications that may meet your requirements, or you can develop something on your own. For example, you might do your documentation using word processing software. The problem of signing or authenticating a note can be solved by printing the note and signing it or adding a secure digital signature. Secure digital signatures are becoming more acceptable, but they require software or hardware to be implemented. There are also applications that capture signatures on an electronic device such as a personal digital assistant (PDA) or notebook computer. If you have ever signed for UPS packages, you have seen this firsthand. If notes are printed, the printed and electronic notes need to match (i.e., any changes or amendments to the electronic note need to be printed as well).

Consider the following when using technology in clinical documentation.

- How will you authenticate the documentation? Will you print and sign everything, capture a real signature in digital format (much like UPS), or will you use a secure digital signature? A mechanism to track any modifications to a record should also be in place.

- Who else needs to review it, and how will they access it? Other clinicians or professionals responsible for the care of your client may need to access records. Will it be from a traditional filing cabinet, through a database, or from a shared drive on your PC or network?

- How will you track or indicate any changes from the original? If an automated solution is not in place (e.g., the computer tracks and records who accessed records, when they were accessed, how long they were accessed), then a policy should be put in place that describes how entries are tracked and accounted for.

- How will you ensure privacy and confidentiality? Will you use a locked file cabinet, password protected PC or network drive, or a signature protected PDA? It's important to articulate a policy for how records will be protected. It is also important to choose good, hard to break passwords (e.g., not using words from the dictionary, using more than six characters, not using a spouse's name or birth date). In addition, passwords should be changed on a regular basis. (See Appendix J, A Look at Privacy and Confidentiality.)

- Does using a technological solution actually help you improve quality, accuracy, cost effectiveness, efficiency, or productivity? Some applications are appealing because of their novelty, but not all applications will make an impact in these areas.

- Where will the documentation be stored or archived? Will you keep paper and digital copies? How long will they be stored, and who will have access after they are archived? A written policy is important for compliance and security purposes.

Clinical Applications

Technological applications for clinical practice include examples such as diagnostic instrumentation clinical software for treatment, and telepractice (i.e., the use of telecommunications technology to deliver professional services at a distance).

The use of technology (e.g., instrumentation, computer applications for treatment) can actually improve the accuracy and efficacy of clinical services. Examples of clinical instrumentation include voice evaluation (e.g., visualizing the laryngeal structure or performing an acoustical analysis of voice), videofluoroscopic or endoscopic dysphagia evaluations, and use of augmentative and alternative communication (AAC) devices. Using instrumentation adds objectivity to clinical diagnosis and treatment, making it easier to identify specific problems, track structural or behavioral changes, and measure outcomes. Diagnostic instrumentation and AAC devices can be expensive, but there are many clinical software applications that require only a PC, speaker, and microphone. These applications (for reading, spelling, word retrieval, auditory comprehension, etc.) can be used as part of a treatment session with a speech-language pathologist (SLP) or for independent practice by clients. The use of most software is enhanced by high resolution monitors and a connection to the Internet.

In addition, the use of technology can help improve productivity by expediting the planning, analysis, and documentation processes.

Telepractice

There is growing support for the use of telepractice to deliver professional services, especially when access to care is an issue (i.e., geographical or mobility considerations). There are emerging reports in the literature of SLPs using telepractice to evaluate and treat a variety of disorders, including fluency (Kully, 2000), voice (Mashima, Birkmire-Peters, Holtel, & Syms, 1999; Mashima, et.al., 2003), dysphagia (Perlman & Witthawaskul, 2002), stroke (Brennan, Georgeadis, Baron, & Barker, in press), and other adult neurological disorders (Duffy, Werven, & Aronson, 1997).

Telepractice can be a helpful service delivery tool in some circumstances (e.g., when access to care is limited due to provider shortages or distance between client and provider). However, there are still several significant barriers to telepractice utilization.

- State Licensing. Since licensing exists to protect the client, a clinician currently needs to be licensed in the client's state.

- Malpractice. Many insurance policies end at state lines. In the event of a lawsuit, there may be questions about where the case will be tried (e.g., one state may have higher award limitations)

- Reimbursement. With the exception of a few state Medicaid programs and third party insurance carriers, telepractice for speech-language pathology services is not currently widely reimbursed. Many programs are grant-funded or support themselves on a private pay basis. Workers Compensation has demonstrated a willingness to contract for such services.

- Confidentiality. While there are ways to secure protected health information (PHI), the client or provider may have concerns about privacy.

- Candidacy. Some clients will not benefit from telepractice based on their condition, support system, or comfort with technology.

- Ethics. Providers need to be qualified and competent in the delivery of any clinical service. Providing clinical services via telepractice requires knowledge and skills that are different from providing face-to-face services.

Telepractice should be considered as simply another tool in a clinical repertoire that is subject to the same standards as any other service delivery model or procedure, including ensuring provider competence, obtaining informed consent, and examining effectiveness and outcomes. In addition, assurance is needed that the equipment and transmission mode being used are of sufficient quality.

Asynchronous (e.g., store-and-forward) techniques involve the capture of data at a remote site, which is stored and forwarded to a clinician for review. Examples of this include an audiogram that is scanned and e-mailed to an audiologist or a voice sample that is sent as a sound file to a voice specialist for perceptual analysis.

Synchronous, or interactive, techniques involve the clinician and client interacting in real time through interactive video or audio. Examples of synchronous encounters include using videophones to provide treatment to stroke clients and using the Internet or closed circuit TV to treat voice clients.

Staff Development

Another important use of technology is in the area of continuing education and staff development. Clinicians in health care settings may have limited opportunity to leave their facility to attend a continuing education activity, but there are technology applications that can contribute to professional development without requiring travel and absence from work. Using technology for continuing education can be a cost-effective way for SLPs to meet various requirements for licensure and certification.

TECHNOLOGY

The Use of Telepractice

Mr. Farmer is 65-years old. He lives with his wife in a rural town 95 miles from the nearest hospital and outpatient center. In the winter, the roads are often impassable. He has been diagnosed with vocal fold nodules, and while he would like to begin treatment in lieu of surgery, he simply cannot commit to traveling the 190 mile roundtrip to visit a speech-language pathologist. He is not homebound, so even if there were a home health provider in his area, treatment would not be covered under Medicare. The SLP at the nearest medical center has a grant-funded telepractice program that enables voice clients to receive voice therapy from their home. It involves one face-to-face evaluation and a home visit by a paraprofessional to help the client and his wife work with the hardware. Therapy is provided twice a week via grant-funded satellite broadband using the Internet. Ultimately, Mr. Farmer's nodules resolved with therapy, and he recovered functional use of his voice in three months and avoided surgery.

Distance learning is becoming more popular. Much like in telepractice, there are synchronous (i.e., instructor and learners interact in real time) activities that clinicians can participate in through teleconferencing and videoconferencing. There are also asynchronous learning models where the content is recorded in audio and/or video format for playback at a later date.

Technology can also be used to facilitate staff development not necessarily related to clinical topics. For example, facilities may post policy and procedure manuals on their organizations, intranet or network. Training required to deal with blood borne pathogens, age specific competencies, and abuse prevention and reporting could be stored and viewed by clinicians at any time.

Beyond formal learning opportunities, there are innumerable resources for continuous learning on the Web. ASHA's Web site has a wealth of information on a variety of topics relevant to SLPs in health care settings. Services such as MedLine or FirstSearch or search engines such as Google or Yahoo may be helpful in accessing abstracts on research articles. (See Appendix K, Tips for Searching the Internet for Resources.)

Administrative Functions

In health care settings, the effectiveness of administrative functions such as scheduling, billing, coding, and analyzing data have a profound impact on the clinicians providing the care. Most readily available office applications (e.g., Microsoft Office, Lotus) have strong administrative functions built into the software. Examples include mail merge, scheduling, and group document editing.

Consider using technology to help administrative functions such as –

- scheduling,
- billing,
- managing productivity,
- managing contacts (e.g., physician lists).

There are many off-the-shelf practice management products and applications that can be used to complete these tasks. There are also software companies that will build a custom application if none of the existing products meets the specific requirements of your facility or department.

While the items listed above are largely considered administrative functions, clinicians will also benefit from these functions. For example, if an appointment is scheduled for a clinician through a central system, the clinician is made aware of the appointment electronically without needing to check voice mail or a physical mail box. In addition, it is possible to include other important information while scheduling the appointment (e.g., medical diagnoses, referral source).

The combined benefits of an automated, integrated system are reflected in terms of Return on Investment (ROI). Assessing ROI involves calculating the cost of providing a service in two different ways. Costs include supplies and materials, time and labor (support and professional staff) as well as other intangible costs such as client dissatisfaction with the old way of doing something.

Using the example of scheduling a client's appointment, we can see how an investment in technology can result in positive returns. The two examples below illustrate two ends of the spectrum.

Low Tech Workflow

A client calls the receptionist in an outpatient clinic, is put on hold for a few minutes, and then makes an appointment. The receptionist takes all pertinent information over the telephone and writes it on a notepad. He then opens the file by re-writing everything on the proper forms. He then fills out an appointment slip and leaves it in the SLP's mailbox. The clinician checks her mailbox at the end of the day and finds the new appointment for the next morning. She needs to do some preparation before she goes home so she is ready for the evaluation in the morning.

The SLP arrives early the next morning to go to the medical records office and review the record. She notices that a videofluoroscopy swallowing study was performed last year and wishes she had time to review it before the evaluation. She then goes to the dietary department to assemble some items for the evaluation. The clinician goes to the reception area, finds a swallowing evaluation form, and fills in all the client information.

When the client arrives, the clinician spends more time filling in the missing information from her record review. They discuss the prior videofluoroscopy, but the client can't remember the details. As the exam progresses, the clinician writes her observations and findings on her report form. At the end of the exam, the clinician shares her findings and recommendations, then rifles through her files to find some education information to copy for the client before he leaves. She tells him that her report should be completed in about a week.

Very High Tech Workflow

The client visits the clinic Web site and chooses a clinician based on the competencies and experience listed in her profile. The client clicks on that clinician's calendar and makes an appointment for the next morning since there is an opening. The client fills out all necessary information securely online and sends the request. Instantly, the clinician gets an appointment notice in her e-mail that links directly to the client's existing medical record already on file with the clinic. The clinician can review complaints, medical history, past treatment, and pertinent social information at that moment without searching for a file. There is even a MPEG video of a videofluoroscopy from 12-months ago that the clinician can view right from her desk. She orders a test tray electronically from dietary to be delivered at the time of the evaluation.

The next morning, the clinician arrives ready for her evaluation. Since the complaint was related to swallowing, the clinician opens up a blank swallowing evaluation report form, which is already populated with the client's information. As the exam proceeds, she speaks into a microphone, and the speech recognition software puts her comments into the appropriate sections of the report. At the end of the exam, the clinician reviews it, and says "print." A copy goes to medical records, the billing department, and to the printer for the client to take home. With the client and family present, the clinician discusses the evaluation results and recommendations, demonstrates swallowing physiology on her PC, and prints education information right from the screen she is in (the system knew she might need it because she was completing a swallowing evaluation).

Practice Automation: What to Consider

Choosing a product or application is an important and somewhat difficult task. Whether it's the use of simple off-the-shelf office applications (e.g., spreadsheets to process billing, databases to keep contact lists, or word processors to write reports), or a more sophisticated application, administrative functions can be greatly streamlined by the right selection. There are a number of considerations that may help determine the best solution, some of which may be unique to a particular setting.

Ease of Use. If the system is difficult to use, it will ultimately fail.

- How easy is the system to use?
- Is the user interface easy to understand and consistent?
- Is it intuitive to you and to your staff?
- Can you easily navigate the system?
- Does the system allow you to enter data in any order?
- Is online help provided?
- How much training is needed for new staff?

Operating System and Platform. The platform will dictate what other types of software are compatible or whether or not there will be licensing fees. Linux, for example, has no licensing fees, but Windows does.

- What operating systems and specific versions are supported?
- What kind of machine (processor, memory, etc.) is recommended by the software vendor?
- What are the licensing fees?

Database. Data from different sources can be combined using databases, and changes can be more easily engineered using compatible databases.

- Is the database that supports the product relational? (Relational databases use open data access standards (e.g., Open Database Connectivity), making it easier to use data with other applications, such as Microsoft Excel.)
- Is the database from a leading vendor, such as Microsoft (Microsoft Access, Microsoft SQL Server) or Oracle?

Networking. In most situations, it is essential to run software over a network so it can be accessed by multiple users. Running software on individual PCs without the benefit of sharing data and other resources (e.g., printers, Internet access) will limit effectiveness.

- Does the software run over a network? If so, what kind—Microsoft Windows Server, Novell?
- Is specialized hardware or software required to run over a network?

Flexibility. Circumstances will change due to regulations, laws, business plans, or policies. A system should be agile enough to respond to these changes.

- How flexible is the software?
- Can you add fields? How many? What types? How easy is it to add a new field?
- Can you customize the windows in the application? Add or hide fields on windows? Change the sort order and filter criteria used on windows?

Insurance Management

- Can you manage the information and procedures you need for insurance companies?
- Are primary and secondary insurance companies supported, and can you de-activate insurance companies when a client switches carriers?
- Can you enter standard rates for insurance companies to automate fee calculations?

TECHNOLOGY

Provider Management

- Can you manage the information and procedures you need for your providers?
- Can you enter standard rates for providers to automate fee calculations?

Scheduling

- Is a scheduling feature provided?
- Is it easy to use and integrated into the application?
- Can you enter charges directly from the schedule?
- Are tools provided to help you schedule appointments (e.g., find available time slots)?
- Can you print your schedule?

Billing

- How easy is the billing process? Is it intuitive?
- Is the process flexible, allowing you to customize billing options to meet the needs of your clients and practice?
- Does the product support billing to multiple parties?
- What tools are provided to help you identify missing payments from clients and insurance companies?

Insurance Filing

- How easy is the filing process? Is it intuitive?
- Is the process flexible, allowing you to customize insurance filing fields to meet the needs of your insurance companies?
- Is electronic filing supported? What is the cost?

Managed Care

- Is a managed care component provided?
- How easy is the process? Is it intuitive?
- Is the process flexible, allowing you to customize managed care processes and the management reporting needs of your practice?

Reporting

- Does the system produce the reports you need to run your business?
- Can you easily export data to other analysis and reporting tools, such as Microsoft Excel?

Document Integration

- Are Microsoft Word templates supported for document creation and integration?

TECHNOLOGY

- Can you store documents created by other applications (e.g., Microsoft Word and others) in your system?
- Does the software provide mail merge capabilities (e.g., for physician mailings or other direct mail activities)?

Technical Support

- Is technical support provided? Is there an 800 number to call? Are there fees associated with support? If so, what are they?
- How quickly are issues resolved?
- Is the technical support staff knowledgeable and friendly?
- Is a maintenance plan available? If so, what is the annual cost?
- Is support available through the vendor's Web site?

Enhancements and Releases

- Does the software vendor provide enhancements and releases on a regular basis?
- Are new releases posted and available for download from the vendor's Web site?
- What are the costs?

Company Information

- Is the software vendor stable and in good financial standing?
- How long has the software vendor been in business?
- Is it committed to the market?
- Who are its competitors?

Cost

- What will it cost? To calculate total cost of ownership, include base software, network costs, costs for additional workstations, costs for multiple providers (some products charge for more than one provider), ongoing technical support and maintenance, and electronic filing costs.
- Are there annual licensing and maintenance fees?

Summary

The wise use of technology in the field of speech-language pathology can help to improve the quality, accuracy, cost-effectiveness, efficiency, and speed of your work. There are solutions for clinical documentation, administrative functions, and continuing education. There are a variety of clinical applications for assessment and intervention of specific conditions as well as the opportunity to provide

TECHNOLOGY

service at a distance via telepractice. In extreme cases, decisions regarding selection and implementation of technology can make or break a clinical practice; therefore, these decisions should be made based on careful research and expert advice.

References

Brennan, D. M., Georgeadis, A. C., Baron, C. R., & Barker, L. M. (in press). The effects of videoconference-based telerehab on story retelling performance by brain injured subjects and its implication for remote speech-language therapy. *Telemedicine Journal and e-Health*.

Duffy, J. R., Werven, G. W., & Aronson, A.E. (1997). Telemedicine and the diagnosis of speech and language disorders. *Mayo Clinical Proceedings, 72(12)*, 1116–1122.

Kully, D. (2000). Telehealth in speech-language pathology: Applications to the treatment of stuttering. *Journal of Telemedicine and Telecare, 6(2)*, 39–41.

Mashima, P. A., Birkmire-Peters, D. P., Holtel, M. R., & Syms, M. J. (1999). Telehealth applications in speech-language pathology. *Journal of Healthcare Information Management, 13(4)*, 71-78.

Mashima, P., Birkmire-Peters, D., Syms, M., Holtel, M., Burgess, L., & Peters, L. (2003). Telehealth: Voice therapy using telecommunications technology. *American Journal of Speech-Language Pathology, 12*, 432–439.

Perlman, A. L., & Witthawaskul, W. (2002). Real-time remote telefluoroscopic assessment of patients with dysphagia. *Dysphagia, 17(2)*, 162–167.

Chapter 7
Personnel
Management

L eaders of successful businesses recognize that valued and satisfied employees are more likely to be productive and less likely to leave the organization. They understand that it is less costly to retain experienced and skilled personnel than to recruit and train their replacements. They seek to prevent the problems associated with employee attrition, such as work flow disruption, increased stress, and decreased morale. Therefore, effective leaders appreciate that successful human resource management is directly related to quality service delivery, productivity, and financial performance.

Chapter Focus

In this chapter, you will learn about **work flow analysis and staffing, performance appraisal, compensation management, disciplinary procedures, professional growth,** and **career advancement**. Whether you are a manager, supervisor, or staff speech-language pathologist (SLP), you can contribute to developing a positive and productive workforce by facilitating consistent open communication about these aspects of employment.

Learning Outcomes

Describe how the organization analyzes work, jobs, and staffing.

Identify the components of successful performance management and appraisal.

Explain compensation management.

Describe training and professional development.

Employee Motivation and Satisfaction

In Chapter 1, Leadership, we described how successful leaders determine the mission, vision, and values of the organization and incorporate the information into daily operations and future planning. The values describe what the organization considers to be important or worthy of emphasis as it fulfills its mission and vision. Major companies as diverse as the Hospital Corporation of America, Ford Motor Company, and Hallmark all include statements about the value of employees to the corporation.

If employees are the most valuable resource of the company, it is important that they are satisfied in their jobs. Leaders who demonstrate care for employees are more likely to find employees reciprocate with improved job performance and loyalty to the company. Some employees assume that salary is the top reason for job satisfaction. However, there are other factors that influence the motivation, satisfaction, and performance of an employee. To evaluate your current job situation, or before accepting a new position, you may consider the following questions:

- Do my knowledge, skills, and experience match the requirements of the job?
- Do I learn new skills or knowledge in my job?
- Does my manager understand my job and reinforce me in a meaningful way?
- Am I on a winning team?

If you answer "yes" to the above questions and you receive fair compensation for your work performance, including salary and benefits, it is likely that you are satisfied in your job.

Work Flow Analysis and Job Description

Work flow analysis entails evaluating the work performed in speech-language pathology, assigning responsibility for performing the work, and evaluating the effectiveness of the job in satisfying the needs of the customer (Bernardin, 2003). The job description is one of those products derived from work flow analysis.

A job description is a written statement of what the jobholder is responsible for doing, under what conditions the work is performed, and what knowledge and skills are typically required to perform the work. Maintaining a current, accurate job description for every position in the organization is essential to–

- identify qualified candidates for the position.
- evaluate the performance of the incumbent.
- guide and protect the organization when making decisions about overtime status (exempt/nonexempt) and job accommodation.

The job description describes the major duties of the job as well as the qualifications or specifications needed to perform the job. This information includes knowledge, skills, abilities, education, credentials, and the amount of autonomy the employee has when performing the work. (See Appendix L for an example of a job description for a speech-language pathologist.)

Staffing Plan

On a routine basis or at least annually, the SLP supervisor or manager analyzes the current and projected volume of work to determine the appropriate staffing levels for the SLP program. This plan takes into account the productivity expectations for each staff member, the number of clients that the total staff is capable of handling, and the current demand for services. For example, if the productivity expectation is that each SLP will spend 60% of worked time in direct client care or contact time, that would mean that a full-time staff member could provide approximately 24 hours of treatment per week (see other discussions on productivity in Chapter 2, Service Delivery, and Chapter 3, Financial Management). In addition, the staffing plan should address how staff absences are handled for vacation, family and medical leave, either by having current staff absorb the client care or by hiring per diem speech-language pathologists.

The staffing plan should provide an analysis of the current client population and forecast future needs in light of the client population and mix and the individual expertise of the staff. To serve outpatient specialty clinics for pediatric feeding, voice, or augmentative and alternative communication (AAC), for example, the staffing plan should ensure that more than one individual has competencies to cover these areas in case of absences or staff turnover. In addition, new case mix opportunities or service delivery trends should be factored into staffing forecasts. For example, the trend toward increased coverage by SLPs on weekends may necessitate a shift in the staffing plan by–

- hiring separate weekend staff.
- rotating schedules for regular staff to cover weekends in exchange for a weekday off.
- modifying weekday schedules (shorter days or one day off) for some staff to cover weekends.

Service industries like health care are labor intensive, meaning that employees' salaries constitute most of the cost associated with providing client care. Therefore, it is important to recruit, hire, develop, and retain productive and talented employees. How do you find and recruit the best people?

Recruitment
When a staff vacancy exists, there is pressure to hire quickly to maintain the continuity of client care and revenue and to ensure that other staff members are not overworked. This rush to relieve the pressure may result in not devoting enough time and attention to the recruitment part of the staffing process.

The recruitment process involves several preliminary steps.

1. Examine why the person left the job and whether the expectations of the position are appropriate. Gather feedback from other team members. If expectations have changed, update the job description.
2. Define the knowledge and skills needed to achieve the desired expectation.
3. Describe the nontechnical characteristics that fit the position, the work team, and the office culture (e.g., team-oriented, good interpersonal skills).

Whether you are a staff speech-language pathologist, manager, or supervisor, you have a contribution to make in the recruitment process. In fact, recruiting is an ongoing process in which you are constantly seeking individuals who add value and talent to your team. Generally, there are opportunities for SLPs to work full time and to fill in on a part-time and as-needed basis to handle fluctuating caseloads, absences, illnesses, or vacations.

Once the job description for the ideal candidate is verified, recruitment efforts should begin as soon as possible and employ a range of methods to recruit the right person. Most organizations have a policy that requires posting internally (formally announcing) vacant positions. This ensures that current staff members are given the opportunity for career advancement. Other recruitment methods include the following:

- Personal contacts in your organization.
- University contacts in targeted speech-language pathology graduate programs.
- Friends and acquaintances in the field or in the community.
- Recruiters and search firms.
- American Speech-Language-Hearing Association (ASHA) - See the Career Center Web site for posting a job and *The ASHA Leader* classifieds.
- ASHA professional services database (ProSearch).
- Other professional magazines, (e.g., *Advance for Speech-Language Pathologists and Audiologists*).
- ASHA Special Interest Division e-mail lists.
- Advertisements in newsletters or on Web sites of state speech-language-hearing associations.
- Announcements placed at educational seminars.
- ASHA's Placement Center at the annual ASHA convention.
- Direct mailings to professionals; addresses purchased from the state association or ASHA.
- Announcements of the position distributed at local continuing education meetings.

- Local newspaper ads in targeted cities.
- The Web page of your organization.

Interviewing

According to Right Management Consultants (2003), interviewing is a sales process in which the employer tries to answer three questions during the course of the interview: CAN this individual do the job? WILL this individual do the job? Does this individual FIT in? Table 7-1 illustrates the areas that the interviewer addresses in order to answer the above questions.

Table 7-1.
Focus of Interview Questions

Employer Questions	Focus of the Interview Questions
Can you do the job?	Skills Knowledge Accomplishments Experience
Will you do the job?	Candidate's interest in the job Short- and long-term goals Work ethic Work style Commitment Availability
Is it a good fit?	Likeability Communication skills Values Appearance Attitude

Management and staff members are looking for someone who meets the needs and challenges of the organization and who also fits into the work team. It is important to involve appropriate staff members in the interview process and to collect timely feedback. While the candidate may be able to do the job and is willing to take the position, the fit is very important. It is not wise to hire a new employee with the idea that in time you will be able to change and mold that person to fit the job and fit in with the team. Just like in a marriage, trying to change another person does not usually work. Prepare your questions in writing and in advance. Asking questions that force the applicant to give examples of his or her behavior in previous jobs will give you the best indicator of future performance. Take notes during the interview process so you can compare the responses of different candidates.

Interview Question Do's and Don'ts

DO ask questions to draw out specific examples of the candidate's experience, work style, motivation, and attitude by eliciting specific responses.

Experience

What assessment instruments have you administered?

How have you made your treatment relevant to an adult's home or work environment (or a child's classroom work?)

Describe a specific case that shows how you have treated someone with (aphasia, brain injury, stuttering, voice disorder, etc.)

Work Style and Relationships

Describe a typical day at work. What challenges do you normally face in getting things done?

What do you do when you have a great deal of work to do in a short amount of time?

Give an example of contributions you have made as a group member.

How would you describe your most recent supervisor's management style? What would you have liked him or her to do differently?

Motivation

Describe a situation when you felt that your contributions were recognized.

Why do you want to leave your present position?

Why are you seeking a job with us?

DON'T ask questions on topics that may violate federal, state, and local laws. For example avoid asking about --

- race or national origin,
- age,
- marital status,
- family status,
- affiliations (religious, political),
- medical or physical condition. (Cole and McNichol, 1997)

An interview is a two-way process. The candidate is also evaluating your organization and the position to determine if there is a match. Therefore, it is important that the manager and staff members share their expectations of the job, the culture of the organization, the work setting, the composition and spirit of the team, the caseload, the positive aspects, and the challenges of the job. It may be tempting to oversell the work situation to a desirable candidate, but it's better to be realistic. Otherwise, the candidate may take the job, determine it isn't perfect, and plan to leave at the first opportunity. Interviews that are open, honest, and interactive produce the best results. Ask good questions and be a good listener.

Selection

After the interview, check references carefully. Explain the job to the person providing the reference, and verify the candidate's answers regarding accomplishments. In larger organizations, the human resources department may require a background check and a drug screen before someone is hired. It is incumbent upon the employer to ensure that credentials, licenses, and academic degrees are verified and accurate. Remember to ask the reference about the candidate's strengths and weaknesses. If a reference is reluctant to share information, at least ask the following questions: *If given the opportunity, would you hire the candidate back again?* and *Is there anything else you would like to tell me about this candidate?* If there is something negative, most people will try to alert you in some fashion. Listen carefully to what the reference says and take notes.

Usually, it is wise to wait at least a week to collect feedback from staff and to evaluate whether the candidate can do the job, will do the job, and is a good addition to your team. In any case, take time to collect enough information to compare candidates fairly and thoroughly. The complete process may involve a face-to-face interview, a phone follow-up, and sometimes a second interview to meet with other decision makers (e.g., appropriate team members, physicians, or administrators) or to clarify certain details or responses.

Trust your intuition, and don't let the pressure of filling the job force you to act too quickly.

Hiring

In making a formal offer to a selected candidate, you should use the job description as the basis for benchmarking the position at a competitive salary. One source for benchmarking is ASHA's Web site, which maintains current data for SLPs' median salary and hourly rates according to geographic distribution. While the position description generally encompasses a salary range, your offer may be higher or lower within the range to reflect individual factors such as candidate's length and type of experience, educational background (e.g., PhD vs. MA), and special qualifications (e.g., bilingual, specialty recognition). In larger organizations, salaries will be determined relative to a "salary scale" (specified pay grades and steps within grades relative to job title and years of experience) to ensure parity with current salaries. If you do not have much latitude in your salary offer, you may be able to negotiate by offering or promoting other benefits of your organization, such as flexible scheduling, paid professional membership dues, licensure fee, tuition reimbursement, on-site continuing education, or a sign-on bonus.

Particularly in times when the number of vacancies for SLPs exceeds the number of SLPs looking for positions, you may need to re-benchmark or conduct a market survey of salaries in your region to advocate for appropriate adjustments.

The completion of the negotiations is confirmed by sending the new employee an offer letter, which states the salary, benefits, and work parameters in broad terms, the start date, and what the employee will need to provide at the time of hire (e.g., graduate studies transcripts). Or the employee may be asked to sign a contract, a legal document that is likely to have more specific details about the nature of the employment.

Orientation

In the first few weeks of employment, employees should be provided a structured orientation program. This is an opportunity to welcome the employee and convey the importance of your work to customers and the organization. The orientation also provides new staff with information about their rights and the expectations of the employer. They are informed about the organization's mission and vision, policies and procedures, and mandated training requirements. In some organizations, an employee is assigned a mentor or team leader to facilitate adjustment to the work environment.

During orientation, the following information may be reviewed:

Organizational overview

- Vision, mission, goals
- Strategic plan

Office functions and logistics

- Computer access and passwords
- Name badge and business cards
- Office access, parking
- Keys to the building and offices
- Tour of work area
- Location of equipment, materials, and supplies
- Phone procedures
- Staff directory and functions

Personnel policies and procedures

- Election of benefits
- Employee handbook
- Dress code
- Leave policies
- Mandatory training schedule
- Performance appraisal process
- Payroll procedures and tax forms

Clinical activities

- Clinical policies and procedures
- Documentation forms and requirements
- Client and staff scheduling
- Billing and insurance
- Clinical competencies
- Staff, team, and educational meetings

A well-organized and comprehensive orientation is a critical element in getting the new employee off to a good start. Some supervisors spread the orientation process over several weeks to enable the employee to learn the information gradually and thoroughly. It also provides ample opportunity to address employee questions and concerns.

Performance Management

Performance Appraisal

Performance evaluations are one component of an ongoing process of providing feedback to the employee. For the supervisor, it is an opportunity to evaluate your effectiveness in hiring and motivating an employee, to recognize the contributions of the employee, and to reinforce his or her value to the organization. A supervisor should complete a performance appraisal at least annually, which may occur on the anniversary date or at a pre-set date for the entire organization. Because the employee's salary may be affected by the results of the performance appraisal, it is essential that appraisals be completed in a timely way and that the process is constructive and instructive.

The performance evaluation addresses three areas of performance:

- **Quality** – demonstrated knowledge and skills related to the key responsibilities contained in the job description.

- **Quantity** – productivity.

- **Interpersonal skills** – sometimes referred to as emotional intelligence (see Chapter 1, Leadership); ability to work well with others.

Rating scales, for example, 5 point scales from "Unsatisfactory Performance" to "Exceptional Performance" are frequently used during performance appraisals to provide feedback on an individual's relative strengths and weaknesses in performing different parameters of the job. Developing behavioral descriptions of the levels of performance for each parameter helps you and the employee ensure that there is a common understanding of the behaviors that constitute unsatisfactory, acceptable, or exceptional performance. This approach also helps assure an objective assessment of performance across employees (Dessler, 1984).

The purpose of the performance evaluation is as follows:

- Express recognition and appreciation for the contributions made by the employee during the year.

- Discuss the employee's performance, including strengths and weaknesses.

- Address the quality and quantity of the employee's work.

- Assess and foster the employee's potential for further advancement and development.

- Build and strengthen the supervisor/employee mentoring relationship.

- Examine how goals and objectives were met during the previous year.

- Plan goals and objectives for the coming year.

Prepare for the performance evaluation by reviewing the job description, results of audits (e.g., clinical chart reviews), notes in the employee's file, and feedback from other staff, clients, and other customers. Ask the employee to evaluate his/her performance prior to the meeting, summarize significant activities and accomplishments, and to report on completion of continuing education and the status of the previous year's goals.

Throughout the year and during the performance appraisal, use departmental clinical competencies as a way of developing and preparing the employee for career advancement. Depending on the SLP's individual interests and the needs of your program, you can establish goals for new clinical competencies or other skills (e.g., student supervision, in-service training, roles in advocacy activities). See Chapter 2, Service Delivery, and Chapter 4, Standards and Compliance for more information about competencies. (See Appendix M for a Performance Appraisal.)

Coaching, Mentoring and Counseling

Coaching, mentoring, and counseling are processes that involve inspiring, teaching, and correcting. Holliday (2001) describes coaching as pushing the employee from behind, counseling as pulling up the employee, and mentoring as walking alongside the employee. He recommends that a supervisor should **coach** when the employee's performance meets standards, **mentor** when the performance is above standard, and **counsel** when the performance is below standard (Holliday, 2001). For more on this topic, also see Chapter 1, Leadership.

Coaching is the process of inspiring and creating an environment that encourages employees to be motivated to achieve results above and beyond their expectations. It is analogous to cheerleading – creating enthusiasm for completing a job or reaching an outstanding goal or result. According to Holliday (2001) successful coaches employ the following tactics with their employees:

- Provide clear and accurate communication.
- Support or "stand behind" the employee.
- Build confidence and positive self-image.
- Foster mutuality and partnership.
- Encourage risk-taking by minimizing punishment for mistakes.
- Have patience for long-term gain.
- Be involved by listening and learning what inspires an employee.
- Build trust and protect confidentiality.
- Show respect for employees as individuals and part of a team.

If the supervisor believes in the employee and communicates confidence in the SLP's ability to achieve a goal, this can result in transforming average performers into the top achieving and most productive speech-language pathologists on your team.

Mentoring is a process that involves instructing and modeling innovative or broader approaches to exemplary employees who want challenge or are preparing for career advancement. With mentoring, the supervisor leads by example to demonstrate personal and job-related excellence to the employee. The employee benefits from the mentor's experience and knowledge of the job, and the organization's politics. It is a more involved and extensive process whereby the supervisor is committed to providing ongoing instruction to the employee. Mentoring is one of the ways that an organization develops talented employees and encourages employee retention.

Counseling is correcting performance that is below the standard. Counseling involves giving and receiving information to correct problems and improve performance to meet department standards. If counseling is ineffective, the supervisor may be required to employ disciplinary procedures.

Training Performance and Disciplinary Action

While a challenging and sometimes uncomfortable process, training performance and taking disciplinary action are among the most important functions of an effective supervisor. It is important to remember that most people strive to do a good job. However, most problems result from or are complicated by a lack of communication between the employee and supervisor. If the supervisor does not clarify job and performance expectations, the employee performs poorly and is generally discouraged and frustrated. If the supervisor does not give timely and meaningful feedback to the employee, the problem is exacerbated to the point that formal intervention is required. However, sometimes even with clear and consistent feedback, the performance does not improve, and intervention is required. The way in which the supervisor and employee approach and handle the situation will affect the ultimate outcome.

Steps to Address Performance Problems

Supervisor and employee meet to –

- determine the cause of the problem (e.g., lack of knowledge or skill; lack of understanding of expectations; lack of motivation; outside factors).

- suggest possible solutions.

- develop a written action plan (problem, steps, and expected outcomes).

- set a time line for evaluating the effectiveness of the plan.

The supervisor plans to meet with the employee when there is adequate time for a discussion and in a place where the meeting will be private and uninterrupted. The supervisor describes the employee's specific performance, focusing on the problem with performance, without attacking the person. The problem or issue is described in as much detail as possible and with as many specific examples as possible. The goal is for the employee to understand clearly the specifics of the problem. It is important to explain the effect that poor performance has on the quality or quantity of the work and on the operation and atmosphere of the work environment.

In discussing performance, be prepared, clear, and direct. Maintain control of the situation by having good eye contact and supportive body language. End the meeting with an expression of confidence in the employee's ability to turn things around and to improve performance. However, if the employee's poor performance continues, formal corrective actions will be necessary. Most organizations follow a progressive disciplinary action policy such as–

- verbal warning,
- written warning,
- final written warning,
- termination.

The disadvantage of progressive disciplinary action policies is that you may not be able to terminate an employee immediately, even for egregious behavior, until you have completed each step. The requirement for following the organization's "due process" ensures that the rights of the individual and the interests of the organization are protected.

It is unfortunate when disciplinary action results in termination; however, it is important that SLPs understand that they are expected to work within the organization's culture and to support the goals of their department or program. When a staff member's behavior or performance is not consistent with the standards of the organization or its culture, this affects the performance and morale of other staff members and the overall quality of the work. Ultimately it can jeopardize the reputation and the success of the organization.

Compensation Management

The organization's compensation policy ensures that employees are paid in a manner that not only is competitive but also meets the staffing and budgetary guidelines of the department. In addition, the policy must be in compliance with the provisions of the Fair Labor Standards Act. To understand how you are paid, you should know whether the organization treats you as an exempt or nonexempt employee. The distinction between nonexempt and exempt employees is as follows:

- **Nonexempt employees** include those employees who are covered by the Federal Wage and Hour Law. These employees are paid on an hourly basis for the number of hours they work each week. They are eligible to receive overtime for hours that exceed 40 hours in 1 week.

- **Exempt employees** include those employees who are specifically exempted from coverage by the Federal Wage and Hour Law. Typically these are professional, managerial, and supervisory employees who are paid on a salary basis. Exempt employees are paid to accomplish all tasks related to their job assignment but are given freedom to work more or less than their allotted work schedule in a week as needed. They are paid based on their FTE (full-time equivalent) status, rather than the exact hours they work each week. You may risk compromising your employees' exempt status if you require them to record their hours worked

In addition to exempt/nonexempt status, a position may also be classified according to the level of responsibility, work schedule, method of compensation, and anticipated duration of employment (e.g., full time, part-time or limited time, limited term, temporary, standby, or on-call). The employer determines what benefits may be offered to individuals in different employee classifications.

The Elements of Compensation

There are two primary types of compensation, direct and indirect. Direct compensation is an employee's monetary reward for work performed. Indirect compensation consists of benefits provided to eligible members of the organization. Direct compensation is an employee's primary form of compensation.

Direct compensation. There are two broad categories of direct compensation: base pay and variable pay.

Base pay is the basic form of compensation, paid on an hourly or salaried basis. Speech-language pathologists who are hourly employees are paid according to the hours worked. Exempt salaried employees are paid for a period regardless of hours worked. Exempt employees do not receive overtime pay, because salary is not time related. In some situations, SLPs may be hired on contract as nonexempt employees and paid on an hourly basis. Unlike salaried employees, these employees are entitled to overtime pay.

Hourly and salaried employees may be offered additional pay on a one-time basis or intermittently throughout employment, or **variable pay**. Variable pay is given to the employee because of individual actions or because of team actions. For example, the SLP might be offered a bonus to accept a position with the organization or as a reward for achieving a certain individual or team utilization rate. Variable pay includes bonuses, incentives, and stock options.

Other forms of compensation. Speech-language pathologists may be compensated for work performed on a per visit basis. Per visit pay is not related either to hours worked or to tasks required for work performed for a salary. Typically, per visit pay is inclusive of time and effort it takes to complete an evaluation, treatment, consultation, required documentation, and any associated travel.

Indirect pay (benefits). Benefits are noncash rewards offered to employees. Federal and state laws require the employer to pay for benefits such as social security, and workers' and unemployment compensation. Other benefits are offered to employees at the discretion of the employer or as a result of collective or individual bargaining. Optional indirect pay may include–

- medical and dental insurance.
- life and disability insurance.
- paid time off.
- retirement, pensions, 401k plans.
- annual professional membership or licensure fees.
- allocation for continuing education activities.

Compensation Systems

You should have a basic understanding about how compensation systems work so that you can make decisions about where to work as well as the long-term job fit. Long-term job satisfaction can be significantly affected by the compensation system utilized by an organization. Look for an organization that not only meets today's salary requirements, but also will continue to meet your needs and work style in the future.

While there is no right way to develop a compensation system, an organization might want to consider the elements of the process for developing a compensation system as listed below.

Step 1. Determine the organization's overall compensation philosophy. There are two contrasting approaches to compensation. A company need not adopt either but may decide that the needs of the organization are best met somewhere on a continuum between the extremes. One approach adopts a pre-established rate or level of compensation, frequently based on length of service and/or years of experience. The federal government and school systems commonly employ these systems. Organizations that adopt this philosophy believe that regardless of what a particular individual might bring to the organization, all new and current employees are entitled to predetermined levels of pay.

On the other end of the continuum is performance-based compensation. Under this philosophy of compensation, an individual's skills, competencies, and performance determine the levels of pay. A tenure or education-based philosophy might be perceived as "fair" to everyone, especially mediocre performers, while a performance-based system might be perceived as "fair" primarily to high performers. The challenge of performance-based systems is to develop objective criteria that equitably measure differences in performance.

Step 2. Compare your pay levels with other organizations in the labor marketplace so that a strategic decision regarding positioning can be made.

After an organization makes its internal decisions regarding pay levels, it is prudent to cross-check the organization's pay levels with similar organizations that employ SLPs. Analyses of pay levels in the marketplace are generally achieved by conducting salary surveys.

Organizations need to decide if they want to employ an above-market strategy (sometimes known as the Third Quartile), a middle-market strategy (known as the Second Quartile), or a below-market strategy (known as the First Quartile). An organization's decision to position itself in one quartile or another is related primarily to the number of potential SLPs available and the company's financial situation.

SLPs who complete their own salary survey in the market where they seek a position will make an informed decision about their own salary expectations. For example, Maria and Paige have comparable experience and skills and take positions with similar companies in the same city. Maria has a higher starting salary than Paige but after two years, Paige's salary is significantly higher than Maria's. This difference could be that Paige decided to take a lower starting salary because she considered the compensation progression policy of her employer and found that, in the long run, she would make more money than if she had worked in the same company as Maria.

Step 3. Determine compensation progression policy. An organization not only must determine what an employee's starting salary will be, but also must make a decision regarding how and why an employee might be eligible for an increase in pay.

- **Pay Grades:** Organizations generally establish pay grades. SLP clinical fellows may be in one pay grade, staff SLPs in another. Then the organization will decide if it will use a few pay grades with broad ranges of salaries (e.g., a range for clinical fellows, staff SLPs, and managers) or many pay grades (e.g., grades for SLPs with progressive "steps" related to different lengths of experience or specialized training). Organizations that use a broad range might give a lot of discretion to the SLP manager to determine if and how much of a pay raise a particular employee might be offered, while an organization with more narrowly defined pay grades may not give as much discretion.

- **Competency-Based Versus Performance-Based Pay Increases:** Organizations using a competency-based method for determining pay grades will focus on the professional growth of the individual SLP and pay accordingly. With performance-based pay, an employee's opportunity for additional pay is related to the individual's or team's ability to achieve a specified goal (e.g., achieving utilization goals). These two methods for determining pay progression are not mutually exclusive. An organization may decide to offer base pay related to achievement of competency and variable pay based on achievement of company goals.

Professional Development

Career Planning

When an organization has a clearly defined career advancement policy, it benefits both the employee and the employer in the following ways:

- Employees can take responsibility for their own professional development.
- Employees have an opportunity to decide their personnel career progression aspirations and link them with the company's expectations and requirements.
- A sense of fairness is fostered as is job satisfaction regarding promotion opportunities.
- Longevity and loyalty are cultivated.
- Employees become active participants in assisting the company to achieve its goals and future strategies.

A career advancement program should include three major components: 1) an organizational description of each position, 2) required behavioral objectives and competencies for each position, 3) the process by which an employee might apply to move from one position to another. Items one and two are discussed below. The application and evaluation process can be unique to each organization.

Job Categories

The size of an organization will influence the number of possible job categories that are available to SLPs. Limitations on number of slots for each job must be clearly stated (e.g., one manager slot and two clinical supervisory slots). Possible job categories might include the following:

- Clinical Fellow
- Staff SLP
- Senior SLP
- Supervising SLP or Team Leader
- Speech Program Manager, Coordinator, or Director
- Rehabilitation Director
- Program Administrative Director
- Other mid-level or upper-level managers and leaders (e.g., compliance officer, vice president, department chair)
- Chief Executive Officer, Chair, or Owner

Competencies

Determining the competencies for each position is a time-consuming and detailed activity. The defined competencies could be clinical, supervisory, leadership, or managerial in nature; job descriptions are not enough. For example, to define the skills of a clinical fellowship supervisor, the job requirement might be to perform successfully the required amount of supervision and complete paperwork for the clinical fellow's application for the Certificate of Clinical Competence. However, competencies might also include the SLP's ability to instill trust, cultivate the talents of others, and provide feedback effectively, as well as an ability to supervise and mentor the Clinical Fellow successfully. In addition, competencies should be achievable. This is especially important if competencies are linked to pay grades. Opportunities for training in the required competency should be included in the policy.

> Competencies should be clearly defined...and achievable.

Training and Continuing Education

Organizations that actively value training and professional development for their employees by devoting the necessary resources are more competitive, innovative, and prepared to ensure that their customers get the best services possible. SLPs and managers who want to provide the best possible service to their clients, customers, fellow employees, and their organizations know that learning is a life-long pursuit. To achieve a competitive advantage and to promote organizational and individual life-long learning, organizations must develop a training, continuing education, and professional development plan. Target training and continuing education may be a part of the strategic plan.

Organizations should have training policies that attempt to answer three essential questions.

- What goals and objectives are to be met by training?
- What types of training will be offered?
- How will training be delivered?

Summary

In a people-centered business like speech-language pathology, employees are the organization's greatest asset. Recruitment and retention of qualified and productive staff members who can do the job, will do the job, and fit in well with the culture of the organization are key business concerns. When considering a position within an organization, it is important to ask about factors that indicate the extent to which the organization values its employees as evidenced by its human resource management and professional development programs.

References

Bernardin, H. J. (2003). *Human resource management: An experiential approach*. New York: McGraw-Hill/Irwin.

Cole, P. A., & McNichol, J. G. (1997). *Tools for a successful job search*. Rockville, MD: American Speech-Language-Hearing Association.

Dessler, G. (1984). *Personnel management: Modern concepts and techniques*. Reston, VA: Reston Publishing.

Holliday, M.(2001). *Coaching, mentoring and managing*. Franklin Lakes, NJ:The Career Press.

Right Management Consultants. (2003). *Career 20/20: Putting your future in focus*. Workshop manual. Philadelphia: Author.

Chapter 8
Marketing

As in other areas of business, speech-language pathology employees are more likely to enjoy job security, competitive salaries and benefits, up-to-date equipment, adequate supplies, and support for continuing education when the organization they work for competes successfully. To improve the financial performance, to compete effectively, and to improve customer satisfaction, the leaders of health care organizations are adopting marketing strategies. Speech-language pathologists (SLPs) benefit personally and professionally from the marketing success of the organization and are expected to contribute to marketing efforts. Consequently, SLPs should understand marketing definitions, principles, and applications so if asked, they can participate in developing or implementing a marketing plan for their departments.

Chapter Focus

This chapter examines the elements of marketing and why they are important to speech-language pathologists. Topics covered include **customer satisfaction**, **complaint management**, **internal and external marketing**, the **purpose of marketing**, and **market research**. We'll also explain the different components and functions of marketing and look at several ways to develop a **marketing plan**.

What is Marketing?

Marketing is the process by which goods and services are moved from the producer or provider to the consumer. It is a multifaceted approach in which you identify the customer's needs, wants, problems, challenges, and goals and then seek to create and exchange products or services that will meet the needs, achieve the goals, and address the problems and challenges. Marketing is more than just advertising. According to Silbiger (1999), marketing is

MARKETING

a circular process with market research at the core. The elements that are affected by research include –

- consumer analysis,
- market analysis,
- competition analysis,
- distribution analysis,
- marketing mix or the 4Ps (**P**roduct, **P**rice, **P**lace and **P**romotion),
- financial analysis,
- monitoring and evaluation.

Marketing Myths

Marketing is important to the success of any business but particularly to those in the service or health care industry. While there are differences between service and manufacturing industries, there are many valuable parallels and applications when it comes to marketing. Perhaps it is useful to compare old definitions and perceptions with more progressive and current thinking. In the manner suggested by Middleton (2003) in his article, *More Clients – A New Marketing Paradigm*, there are new ways to think about marketing, described in Table 8-1.

Table 8-1.
A New Marketing Paradigm

Old Thinking	Current Thinking
Marketing is manipulating customers into buying goods or services that they don't need.	Marketing is making people aware of services that could make a positive difference in their lives.
Marketing involves professionals bragging about themselves and putting down their colleagues.	Marketing is a valuable service because it provides people with information and options.
Marketing is dishonest and makes bold promises to justify over charging people.	Marketing is honorable and helpful because it offers solutions to problems that may be costly and time consuming to the customer.
Marketing requires increased cleverness in order to get attention and a response.	Marketing requires an understanding of the customer's problem, challenges, and goals in order to plan appropriate solutions and interventions.
Marketing costs a lot of money for nothing.	Marketing involves analysis and planning to ensure the amount invested produces positive, cost effective results.
Marketing is competitive, so it requires sneaky and secret methods and activities.	Marketing offers opportunities to cooperate and joint venture with other professionals to benefit the consumer.

MARKETING

What do these definitions and "new thinking" mean to the practice of speech-language pathology? Basically, marketing is the way in which we meet the needs and wants of our customers. Our customers may include clients, caregivers, general public, physicians, referral sources, third-party payers, case managers, coworkers, donors, volunteers, managers, supervisors, directors, administrators, owners, board members, university personnel, legislators, business and community leaders, and members of the media—anyone with whom we communicate or interact to provide our services.

Internal and External Marketing

Internal marketing occurs when employees are empowered, encouraged, and expected to share the features and benefits of SLP services with the individuals who work in their department, facility, or organization. These internal customers might include –

- coworkers,
- team members,
- referring physicians (may also be external customers),
- administrators,
- public relations personnel.

Internal Marketing

Sobia is invited to present at the physicians' lunchtime case conference about the role of speech-language pathologists in working with swallowing disorders. Among the audience are several new medical residents working in the outpatient clinic. She shows videos illustrating diagnostic techniques, treatment, and functional swallowing improvement in patients with neurologic and post-surgical conditions. The next week, she receives 3 referrals from the new residents.

The opportunity to educate others about the benefits of speech-language pathology services occur during daily work activities such as before or after treatment sessions; discussions in the hallway or elevator; during physician rounds, and clinics; in phone calls and e-mails; and in clinical documentation. Other opportunities include in-service presentations, conferences, continuing education activities, and student supervision.

Speech-language pathologists may employ internal marketing methods by communicating the following information to internal customers:

- Quality and scope of your services
- Positive client outcomes
- New equipment and technology
- Timeliness of scheduling and care
- Improved customer satisfaction
- Individual and group treatment options
- Convenient hours and accessibility to service
- Success stories

MARKETING

Marketing

121

When employees are motivated or provided incentives to engage in activities that increase referrals or support program goals, the likelihood increases that they will be comfortable with internal marketing. Employees perceive that their performance and commitment are valued and noticed by the employer. The separation of employees by titles, disciplines or walls is increasingly being replaced with a sense of teamwork and a common purpose. (For more on employee relationships, see Chapter 7, Personnel Management.)

External marketing involves educating and sharing the value and benefit of SLP services with external customers or individuals outside of your organization. External customers might include –

- clients,
- caregivers,
- community physicians, other than referral sources,
- the public,
- federal, state, or local legislators,
- media,
- government and regulatory agency personnel,
- insurance company personnel,
- case managers.

We will return to this topic in our discussion of marketing mix and promotion later in this chapter. In addition, Chapter 9, Advocacy lists effective methods for influencing groups and decision makers. Suggestions for media resources for marketing your business are also available from ASHA.

External Marketing

Promotion of your services to external customers may involve advertising your services in the Yellow Pages, sharing a compelling client success story with the local television station, offering free speech and language screenings to hospital employees during *May – Better Hearing and Speech Month,* and participating in a case manager trade show in which you host a booth describing speech and language services at your facility.

Customer Service and Complaint Management

Marketing seeks to meet customer needs or wants through exceptional customer service. Successful marketing starts with and focuses on the clients and their caregivers. Before describing the marketing process, it is important to emphasize the value of exceptional customer service and effective complaint management.

Excellent customer service begins with each employee in each organization or company. Your attitude towards customers and coworkers influences your verbal and nonverbal behavior. Positive results start with a positive attitude.

Complaints. The most common reasons for complaints are that products and service fall short of expectations, someone is rude or indifferent, or the provider simply does not listen to the client. According to TARP, a company that measures customer satisfaction and loyalty, the average complaint is shared with 10 people, and for every one complaint received, the average company has 26 unhappy customers who never report their complaints. However, the good news is that 70%-95% of the people who complain and receive prompt resolution of the problem will return to the organization or company for continued service (TARP, 1999).

To manage a problem or complaint,

- sincerely thank the client for his or her feedback.
- collect pertinent information by listening carefully, maintaining eye contact, and taking notes, if needed.
- put yourself in the client's shoes; demonstrate empathy, interest, and acceptance of the complaint.
- apologize in tangible terms that reflect your understanding and ownership of the problem.
- exhibit a can-do attitude by resolving as much of the problem as you can control and ensure there is follow up with action outside of your control.
- verify that the customer is satisfied with the response and plan of action.
- communicate the situation to your supervisor, explain the action taken, and discuss ways to prevent similar problems.

Market Research

The purpose of market research is to determine if anyone is willing to buy your services and if your services will meet the needs of the customers, clients, and their families. Market research is an ongoing process. The information generated is used in the initial planning and development as well as in future decisions to improve, modify, discontinue, or expand your services. Market research is also valuable in convincing others to invest in your services or projects. For example, the chance of getting approval for a $250,000 expansion of your voice and swallowing center is enhanced dramatically if you include accurate and pertinent market research data in the program proposal.

Market research involves finding the answers to the following questions:

- Who are the customers?
- Are the current products, services, or equipment meeting customer needs?
- What is the difference between your service and those of the competition?
- How many competitors and what types of competition exist?
- How can you differentiate your service from your competition?
- How large is the market or population of people willing to buy or be referred for your service?

- What are the industrial, regulatory, legislative, or organizational trends that could affect your business or referrals?
- What is the impact of technology on your business and position in the marketplace?
- How do clients access your service and how do you facilitate the process?

Because most SLPs don't have the financial or decision-making resources for expensive research studies or initiatives, it is important to use tools that are inexpensive and accessible. There are a number of resources available including ASHA; federal, state, and local government agencies; libraries; university business schools; and the Internet.

Consumer Analysis

Customer Type. Remember that marketing is based on satisfying or meeting the needs and wants of the customers. In marketing, customers are divided into four groups.

- User
- Decision maker
- Buyer
- Influencer

For example, **users** of speech-language pathology services are individuals who have speech, language, cognitive, voice, fluency, swallowing, and other communication disorders; however, these individuals may not decide whether service is justified or needed. The **decision maker** may be the parent, spouse, caregiver, or physician. Therefore, marketing efforts should focus on educating and convincing the decision maker about the value of speech-language pathology services.

The **buyer** may be someone other than the decision maker. For example, an insurance company approves and pays for speech-language pathology services. Without case manager approval, the third-party payer will not reimburse the provider for SLP services even if the client, caregiver, and physician decide that services are needed. In this case, marketing efforts are focused on establishing a relationship, educating, and convincing the case manager, who works for the insurance group, about the benefits of speech-language pathology services.

Then there is the influencer. **Influencers** may be many and difficult to identify. For example, an insurance executive or his or her child receives exceptional SLP services. The outcomes are impressive, and the services are provided in a cost effective and efficient manner. The SLP exhibits excellent interpersonal skills and shares a brochure indicating the multiple and convenient locations of the company's services. The insurance executive is in a position to influence the expansion of speech-language pathology service providers to include this SLP and his or her company. Therefore, it is worth the time and energy to follow up and focus marketing efforts on individuals who influence final purchasing decisions.

Customer Profile. The next step in the consumer analysis is to develop the customer profile for the most valuable customers. These data will have an impact on the services and programs that you choose to pursue. Information is collected in the following areas:

- Demographics – age, gender, income, family status, ethnic distribution, geographic location, and other common census classifications.
- Psychological Characteristics – interests, opinions, motivation, and attitudes.
- Social – family life cycle, social class, and culture.

Demographic data are valuable because they more fully describe the characteristics of potential buyers and users of speech-language pathology services. The more you know about your buyers, the more effective you will be in developing your marketing plan. For example, baby boomers, people born between 1946 and 1964, represent more than 10% of the U.S. population. They make decisions about health care for themselves, their children, and their parents. They may be the focus for promotional activities about nursing home services for their parents. They may be unable to transport their parents for outpatient speech-language pathology services. You may consider expanding your services to home health care or arranging client transportation to your facility. Baby boomers are also entering the age when memory loss may be a concern. You may target this population as you develop memory workshops or workbooks.

Psychological factors affect people's buying habits, but it is not easy to identify and measure these variables. Opinions, attitudes, interests, and motivation differ from person to person. However, it is valuable to consider these factors as you plan and develop your services. For example, more people seem to prefer the comforts of home and are computer literate. Therefore, you may explore offering telepractice as an alternative or in addition to traditional clinical services in speech-language pathology. (See Chapter 6, Technology for more on telepractice.)

Social characteristics may factor into buying decisions, such as whether a family can afford SLP services not covered by insurance. You may consider whether your target population is single, married, with or without children, or widowed. Some research indicates that upper class or higher income earning individuals do more comparison research before buying. They may also be able to afford uninsured services. A reading readiness program that is private pay may be more successful in an affluent neighborhood. Other social factors should be considered. For example, the Hispanic population is the fastest growing subculture in the United States, so it may be wise to learn more about this culture and the best way to communicate information about your services to this group.

Purchasing Behavior. The last consideration in consumer analysis is purchasing behavior. In health care, it is important to examine the purchasing behavior of individuals as well as groups or organizations. Now that we have answered the question Who are my customers?, it is important to ask additional questions that will further identify and define the target customers.

What are the benefits of your service to the person or the organization? What is the motivation for using your service? For example, a client who had a stroke wants SLP services for more than the ability to use one-sentence utterances in conversation, 90% of the time. He or she wants to know that you will provide services that will enable him or her to live at home independently, to return to some type of gainful employment, or to participate in social activities and interactions.

Why does a customer decide to use your service over that of your competition? Why does the manager of provider relations for a local insurance company decide to add you to the provider list? It may be that your rates are competitive, and your client outcomes are the most functional and impressive. A son may drive his father to the facility that also provides physical and occupational therapy because it is more convenient. He may not understand or be concerned about the quality of care because convenience is the primary reason for his decision. It is important to consider why customers choose your service.

When to Provide Services

The question of when may also refer to the stage in the customer's life cycle. For example, senior citizens may be interested in workbooks with interesting memory and word-finding activities. In this example, clients over 65 years of age may be your target consumers.

When should you provide services, and when should you promote the purchase of your services? For example, a laryngectomy client may benefit from a preoperative visit as well as post-operative care. In this case, the client's physician is your target consumer. Early morning and weekend services may be convenient for working parents seeking SLP services for their children. The parents are the target consumers, and convenient treatment hours will be the benefit that you emphasize.

Where should the channels of distribution be to ensure they are accessible? A client may prefer swallowing treatment through a home health agency rather than traveling to an outpatient facility. However, parents may be willing to drive their child across town to a facility known for its treatment of stuttering.

How does a person go about looking for your service? Does he or she follow the recommendation of the physician, insurance company, or neighbor? Does a parent or family member look under speech-language pathology services in the Yellow Pages?

MARKETING

Market Analysis: Segmentation Versus Mass Marketing

Market analysis involves looking at customers as groups and considering how size and trends will affect them. An organization or individual may choose to market to the general public, a target population, a segment of the population, or multiple segments. This information will determine the **marketing mix** and strategies that are employed to encourage the customer to buy or use the service.

It's helpful to identify and classify the market segments by needs and demands. For example, a speech-language pathologist decides to start her own private practice or company. She begins by identifying potential markets such as skilled nursing facilities, hospitals, public schools, private schools, charter schools, home health agencies, and private clients. She then looks at each segment, evaluating –

- the client base,
- the services needed,
- the time needed to provide those services,
- the potential for profit.

She would also consider market trends that may affect each particular segment. For example, a decrease in Medicare or Medicaid reimbursement may decrease the demand for SLP services to skilled nursing facilities.

The next step in market analysis is to choose the target market, segment, or niche market and develop marketing tactics. The following are some guidelines:

- **Aim for your most likely successes**. Start with an easy market or one in which you are more likely to succeed. This may be a market in which you, or your organization, will have an advantage. A speech-language pathologist may choose to contract with a hospital on an as-needed basis to provide videofluoroscopic swallow and adult rehabilitation services because she is a recognized expert in these areas.

- **Capitalize on a trend or regulation change**. You may discern that with recent increases in Medicare reimbursement for swallowing studies, there is more potential to make a profit, and you may decide to focus on hospital contracts.

- **Choose a market that is underserved relative to demand**. For example, you may have expertise in the treatment of children who stutter. You decide to offer traditional speech-language pathology individual and group services and a technology or computer assisted treatment intervention. You may be the only facility in your community to offer both options to potential customers.

- **Be selective**. Because of the time investment and money involved in marketing, develop one market at a time.

- **Be flexible**. If circumstances change, don't be afraid to change the market focus.

- **Become a recognized brand**. Remember to develop a service that is positioned well. In other words, choose a market in which your service stands for one thing and that one thing is easy for the customer to remember. Services designated as "centers of excellence" are positioned well in the health care industry. This designation may be related to a variety of factors such as uniqueness of the service, comprehensiveness of the team, knowledge and expertise of the providers, and specialized and technologically advanced equipment. In medical center training programs, there are specific criteria defining centers of excellence. Examples of well positioned services or centers of excellence in SLP might include a cleft palate clinic, voice or swallowing center, stuttering program, or center for augmentative and alternative communication.

Analysis of the Competition

It is important to understand the competition or what factors or entities in your environment are capable of affecting or disrupting your business. In other words, what will cause your customers to choose or switch to another provider of speech-language pathology services? The one thing we can reliably predict about the weather and health care services is that they will change. It is important to anticipate competitive changes and plan to respond to them.

There are many types of competition in business. They range from a sole provider of a special service or product or **monopoly** to multiple providers of a similar service or **open competition**. With open competition, price and accessibility are important factors. Monopolies occur infrequently, and government regulation is usually needed to prevent price gouging. In these situations, the product or service is unique and may be patented. An example of a monopoly in health care is a patented drug for which a pharmaceutical company charges high prices to cover costs associated with research and development. While they are not exactly monopolies, the following are examples of very specialized procedures, equipment, or facilities in speech-language pathology:

> In the business community and health care industry, there is increased interest in building formal or informal relationships.

- Passy-Muir valve – a widely used brand of speaking valve
- Tracheal-esophageal puncture (TEP) – a common procedure for individuals undergoing laryngectomy
- Children's hospitals – the preferred setting for children under 18 years

To evaluate the competition in speech-language pathology and to prepare to market your services, collect the following information:

- **Identify the competitors**. Learn the names of the competitors, how they operate, which customers use their services, what they offer, where they are located, when they provide service, and why customers prefer them.

- **Analyze their strengths and weaknesses**.

- **Investigate more completely why the competition is successful**. Consider the reasons, such as price, location, customer service, selection and variety, quality, client outcomes, referral source relationships, better reimbursement, or innovative promotional activities. Consider whether lowering prices will help or hurt your business relative to your competition. Generally, lowering price is not an effective strategy.

- **Understand how the competition is positioned in your service area**. In other words, one hospital may be known for having the best voice center in town. Is it because of the medical director's reputation, the amount and type of research conducted, innovative diagnostic procedures, up-to-date and expensive equipment, effective and ongoing advertising, or a combination thereof? Is this position impenetrable, or is there opportunity to establish a differential advantage?

An interesting paradigm shift appears to be emerging in the business community and the health care industry. There is increased interest in building formal (mergers) or informal (networking) relationships with competitors. A win-lose strategy is being replaced with a win-win strategy. Instead of spending precious funds on competing with other providers, leaders are increasingly forming coalitions and alliances that are mutually beneficial. However, the key is to find the right balance in these relationships. To give away business and lose money will ultimately result in your inability to provide needed care in speech-language pathology.

Distribution Channels

Distribution describes how products or speech-language pathology services reach our clients. As described earlier, because a client will benefit from SLP services, it does not follow that he or she will receive the needed care. For example, a client has a stroke and exhibits mild to moderate aphasia and dysarthria. Treatment may be disrupted by the following circumstances:

- The client may not recognize the need for or want to receive speech and language services because he or she is embarrassed or not ready to deal with the communication disorder.

- A family member may not want medical or health care intervention of any kind and refuses to allow the client to participate in treatment.

- The physician feels spontaneous recovery will occur and sees no reason to refer the client for SLP services.

- The employer does not cover SLP services in the health care plan, and the client lacks alternative resources for coverage.

- The case manager from the insurance company does not authorize coverage of SLP services beyond a couple of visits.

Does this sound familiar? This is why speech-language pathologists should be familiar with the distribution channels of their services. They should understand the decision makers and influencers at every step in the process. The SLP should advocate, communicate, educate, document, and persevere through the distribution process to ensure that the client receives appropriate services in a timely and effective manner.

Development of the Marketing Mix

Just like the manufacturing industry, the health care industry has many factors that affect the desired level of sales. The mix of these variables is known as the marketing mix or the 4Ps. They are **P**roduct, **P**rice, **P**lace and **P**romotion (see Table 8-2).

At this point in the marketing plan, you have examined the consumer, the market, the competition, and the distribution. It is time to develop an action plan in which you combine the 4Ps to increase referrals and use of SLP services.

Product Positioning, and Branding

It is important to define the breadth and depth of the product or service that you provide. Subsequent marketing decisions will depend on this component of the marketing mix. The steps outlined below will help you to define your product or service.

Describe services in tangible terms

What are the products or services that you offer to consumers or clients? Speech-language pathology services and their benefits are largely intangible. Therefore, it is important to describe the tangible benefits we deliver to the client. For example, describe how the client's life will be more independent, productive, and enjoyable as a result of your intervention. If the target is the third-party payer, describe how the service provides functional client outcomes and high customer satisfaction at a reasonable cost.

Explain how the service differs from the competition

Articulate the different advantages that you offer to the consumer or customer. What unique features characterize your SLP services? Consider the following advantages and choose the traits that apply to your service:

- Knowledge or experience of the provider
- Cost savings

- Competitive prices
- Convenient hours
- Prompt scheduling
- Related services offered in the same location
- Impressive outcomes or results
- New technology
- Clinical specialties
- Association with a reputable hospital, physician or clinic
- One of a kind service in the area
- Exceptional customer service
- Special award or recognition

Table 8-2.
The Marketing Mix or the 4Ps of Marketing

	Definition	Considerations
Product	The goods or services offered by the organization. What you do to distinguish your service in the mind of the customer.	Needs and wants of the customer or consumer. What does your service stand for? How does it compare to similar services?
Price	The amount the customer is willing to pay for the service. Reimbursement required by the organization to remain in business.	Fixed and variable costs. Reasonable and customary charges for the area. Competition
Place	Access to the service. The manner by which services are distributed to the customer.	Location of the service. Obstacles to obtaining service.
Promotion	Communication to the market or customer that the organization is able to meet needs or solve problems or challenges.	Ways to make your product visible and desirable such as – • advertising, • personal selling, • publicity and PR, • sales promotion, • direct selling.

MARKETING

Determine the product and service life cycle

Services, like products, have a period of time that they are in the market. A new service progresses through the introductory phase, the growth period, the maturation phase, and the decline. The position of your service in the life cycle will influence the product quality and mix, the price, the promotional activities, and the location of the service.

Consider Branding and Positioning

Branding is the personality or feature that distinguishes your product or service in the mind of the consumer. It may be a name or symbol. For example, Kleenex means facial tissue, and Xerox means copying machines. The star on a professional football player's helmet signifies the Dallas Cowboys, and Clydesdales drawing a sleigh signify Budweiser. The value that a brand name gives a product is referred to as brand equity. In health care, certain providers such as Sloan-Kettering, the Cleveland Clinic, or Mayo Clinic have **brand equity**. Speech-language pathologists starting their own company should choose a name that differentiates it from the competition, is memorable, and defines the business.

Positioning is what you do to differentiate the product in the mind of the consumer. You may want to position your service to appeal to the largest number of customers or to a niche market. You can also position your brand to be more competitive. For example, Tylenol was not the first aspirin; it was the first nonaspirin pain reliever. Some products can also use an established brand name against a competitor. For example, Scope advertisements used the term "medicine breath" to the disadvantage of its primary competitor, Listerine.

Consider Regulatory Issues

State and federal regulations govern certain business practices. Some of these regulations may have an impact on the marketing mix. For example, the Trademark Law Revision Act grants a company protection of a trademark or brand name as long as the name is registered before it is used. A trademark or brand name is valuable to a company. It is important to know if anyone else is using the name and to register it with the government. Find out more about copyrights and trademarks at the U.S. Patent and Trademark Office's Web site http://eteas.uspto.gov.

Price

Intelligent pricing is the key to the success of any business. Pricing affects the business's profit and survival in a competitive market. Determining the appropriate price or charge for your service requires research, preparation, and analysis. Consider the following steps:

- Determine your position. Positioning determines the price of your service. If your service is perceived to be valuable, the consumer may be willing to pay a

> Branding distinguishes your service...giving it value.

higher price. A good example is clothing with a designer label or logo. Consider what can be added to your service to increase its value or worth to the customer.

- Take into account the prevailing market price for your service and not what you wish you can charge, along with the factors discussed in Chapter 3, Financial Management related to determination of fees based on costs.

- Evaluate pricing constraints such as demand for the service, position in the life cycle (new, growing, mature, or declining product or service), and the nature of the market structure (highly competitive to monopoly).

- Determine if your pricing objective is to make a profit, maximize sales or volume, gain market share, or to price high or low to create an image. Wal-Mart, for example, uses low pricing as part of its image.

- Evaluate cost and volume variables. The key to making a profit is to sell your service above what it costs. The challenge here is to identify and compute all the costs accurately and completely. Break-even analysis is one way to evaluate pricing for a service. Simply stated, break-even analysis is a mathematical formula that tells how much service you must sell for your company or department to break even. The actual cash collected must equal the cash expended. You must identify fixed costs (rent) and variable costs (utilities). Project sales or how many units of service are needed to break even taking into account fixed costs, variable costs, and fees charged (see Chapter 3, Financial Management).

Place

Place refers to where you offer your service. It also takes into account who is eligible for service, the distribution of service, and the obstacles to obtaining service. As discussed previously, there are many decisions and approvals that are required to access speech-language pathology services. The process may involve physicians, third-party payers, employers, or regulatory agencies as well as completion of specific forms and documentation. You should feel encouraged to educate, advocate, and guide the client and caregiver to expedite the process and to increase the chances that needed services are provided and covered by third-party payers.

The physical location of the SLP clinic or department also gives the customer a perception of the quality and worth of the service. There should be easy access to parking and accommodations for people with disabilities. It may be advantageous to locate SLP services adjacent to or near other needed rehabilitation services like physical and occupational therapy. Multiple sites may be considered to expand access to a particular service.

Promotion

The goal of promotion is to affect the behavior and meet the needs of the buyer or customer. Therefore, it is important to define the target customer. As mentioned earlier, identify who makes the final buying decision that allows the customer to use your service. Will you sell directly to the client or to other decision makers in the distribution process? For example, you may decide to focus promotional efforts on case managers who work for insurance companies because they are the decision makers that approve speech-language services. It is important to determine the promotional mix or strategy for each customer or market segment. Remember that each strategy involves effective communication and education to be successful. Here are the promotional strategies most typically used.

Advertising includes newspapers, magazines, radio, television, and outdoor billboards. Usually, advertising is paid and impersonal, but it is controlled by the organization that buys it. In the past 10 years, advertising has become more accepted and utilized by health care organizations. The Yellow Pages is another means of advertising as is the distribution of business cards and stationery.

Personal selling usually means personal contact with the buyer through a direct sales force or sales representative or agent. Another personal selling method is through a "lead blocker," a person or strategy that you use to knock down a barrier to a certain market. For example, you may have expertise in the treatment of stuttering. However, you don't have the money to advertise your services to the general public. You may feel delayed auditory feedback devices have some merit for select clients who stutter and decide to dispense these devices to enter this market. The manufacturer of the device advertises you as a distributor, and you develop an agreement that also allows you to offer other stuttering treatment, if indicated. Personal selling also occurs at trade shows.

Publicity and public relations present ideas that may indirectly promote and sell your service. Publicity is usually unpaid; it may be a personal interest story, a news story, press release, press conference, celebrity spokesperson, or poster child. Ultimately, the message may not be controlled by you. It is the promotional tool or management of communication between your service and a broader audience or market, but it can be an effective way to increase awareness about communication disorders or some unique, new service.

Sales promotion activities such as coupons, refunds, contests, and samples reinforce advertising.

Direct selling includes direct mail (fliers, handbills, brochures and postcards), junk mail, e-mail marketing, Web sites, fax marketing, telemarketing, infomercials and shopping networks.

You should decide early in the market plan development whether you will link your business to the Internet. Do you want your service to take advantage of all high-tech business options like interactive TV, smart cards, and Web sites? If you want to develop a Web site, you should consider the functions you would like to perform on it.

- Sell your product or service – a transaction site.
- Promote your service – a promotional site.
- Provide information and suggestions – a content or educational site.
- Solve customer complaints.
- Combine some of the functions listed above.

Keep in mind that the promotional mix of advertising, personal selling, publicity, sales promotion, and direct selling may vary depending on whether you are trying to promote your product or service, the place of the sale, or the price of your service. You should specify the differences in the marketing plan.

Financial Analysis

The financial component of the marketing process may be the most important because it determines whether your marketing efforts are making or losing money. Let's assume that you have defined your customer. You are clear about the service that you plan to market. You have developed your position statement or how you want your customer to perceive and differentiate your service from the competition. You have evaluated the trends and size of your market. You understand the impact of competition. You identified the decision makers at every stage of the distribution channel. You have defined "the 4Ps" of the marketing mix. However, you don't know if you can afford to implement your marketing plan and may not be able to project with certainty whether you will make or lose money in the process. How will you find the answers?

According to *The Ten Day MBA* (Silbiger, 1999), you must address the following three issues:

- What are the costs?
- What is the break-even point?
- How long until the investment is repaid?

Financial considerations were addressed previously under Marketing Mix and in Chapter 3, Financial Management. The principles for break-even analysis involve the identification of fixed and variable costs.

For example, let's consider a proposal for a $250,000 investment in your voice and swallowing center. You need to determine the volume of clients and the collected revenue required to break even or to cover the fixed and variable costs associated with the new service. The cost of market penetration and promotional activities are included in the computation of total costs. An alternate approach is to separate out the volume of new referrals or business and to determine if the new revenue covers the fixed cost of the marketing plan for the voice and swallowing center.

Also consider how long it will take to recoup the cost of offering a full service voice and swallowing center, including marketing and promotional activities. How many years of operation are required to generate a profit? What is the payback period on the $250,000 investment? For example, if the center generates $50,000 profit per year, it will take 5 years just to get back the investment. However, the goal is to generate profit on top of the investment. You may need to rethink the marketing plan. This leads us to the final component of the marketing process.

Monitor and Revise the Marketing Strategy

In a changing health care environment, it is important to anticipate the impact of changes and to revise the marketing plan accordingly. The components of the marketing mix are monitored closely and modified, as needed. Don't be afraid to discontinue a marketing tactic that is not working. For example, you may choose to end participation in a local health fair or screening program because you do not receive follow-up referrals to your center and you can't afford the cost of sending staff members to participate and represent your organization.

When an organization revises and reviews the strategic plan, there should be a systematic and objective review of the marketing plan. The market plan analysis includes reviewing market segments and conducting a **SWOT** analysis (**S**trengths, **W**eaknesses, **O**pportunities and **T**hreats) (see also Chapter 1, Leadership) of the organization, competitors, products and services, price, promotion, and the channels of distribution.

Table 8-3.
Sample Marketing SWOT Analysis

Product	Strength	Weakness	Opportunity	Threat
Dysphagia Treatment Program	Physician presentations Workshops Nursing education	Outdated brochure	Special interest story Open house in May	Budget cuts
Pediatric Speech-Language Treatment	Letters to referral sources Word of mouth network Parent support group meets in the facility	Mass mailing Group physician presentations – poor participation	Special interest story on TV Presentation to child advocacy group	Budget cuts Competition has initiated a TV advertising campaign

Of course, it is important to include quantitative objectives in the development of the marketing plan to facilitate this analysis. Be prepared to change the marketing strategy to respond to the changes in health care and specifically, in speech-language pathology.

The Marketing Plan

Marketing plans generally contain three similar components: marketing objectives, strategies, and action steps. A marketing plan begins with an analysis of the organization's entire operation. Following that, decisions are made about the markets, products, and services to emphasize. As a speech-language pathologist, you may be involved in developing or giving input into the overall strategic plan for your organization or department. An essential part of the strategic plan is the development of a marketing plan. It is as important as the financial, production, and human resource components of the strategic plan of your organization.

Sample Marketing Plans

Berkowitz (2004) suggests the following outline for a marketing plan:

- Management Summary – Summarize the marketing strategies for the specific service or program. What are the action steps and the results for the next year?

- Economic Projections – Analyze economic trends or factors that could affect the marketing of this service. Consider employment, personal income, business expectations, and inflationary pressures.

- The Qualitative Market – Consider the customers for this service. Include demographic information.

- The Quantitative Market – Weigh the potential demand for the service. Include numbers of customers, dollar volume of the business, target market, and where you stand competitively at the present time.

- Trend Analysis – Review historical trends. Where are you headed?

- Competition – Define your current competitors. Why are they successful? Action for the coming year.

- Problems and Opportunities – Examine the problems that might inhibit the marketing of the service. Are there opportunities that you are not pursuing?

- Objectives and Goals – Determine where you want to go with this service. State the short- and long-term goals in qualitative and quantitative terms.

- Action Programs – Think about what you must do to reach the goals that you established for this service, given the economy, market, and competition. Include market penetration and promotional activities like advertising and direct mail.

Each action step should include the schedule for completion, method of evaluation, and the person responsible for executing the program and for measuring results.

There are other guidelines for developing a marketing plan, such as the more simplified outline found in the *FastTrac New Venture Manual* (Ewing Marion Kaufman Foundation, 1995). It includes the following components:

- Industry profile
- Current market size
- Growth potential
- Industry trends
- Competition profile
- Customer profile
- Customer benefits
- Target markets
- Market penetration methods

In *The Marketing Plan*, Luther (2001) describes how to prepare and implement a marketing plan, attending to the following planning elements:

- Plan strategic position
- Marketing personnel
- Marketing objectives and strategies
- Product or service plan
- Marketing communication
- Research plan
- Internet plan
- Customer service plan
- Sales management plan
- Budget and timing plans and action plans

Summary

In this chapter, we have explored the reasons for marketing in speech-language pathology services and the key elements and processes involved in developing a marketing strategy and plan. We have considered the 4Ps of marketing, including Product, Price, Place, Promotion and have provided guidelines for the kinds of questions and decisions that go into designing a marketing plan. Marketing has both internal and external customers. Clinicians who work for an organization play an important role in implementing the marketing strategies with both of these groups. The degree to which you satisfy the needs and wants of clients will have a direct bearing on their satisfaction which, in turn, will affect the outcome of your treatment, the perception of your job performance, the payment for your services, the likelihood of repeat business and referrals, the financial viability of the organization, and, ultimately the perception of the profession of speech-language pathology.

References

Berkowitz, E. (2004). *Essentials of health care marketing*. Sudbury, MA: Jones and Bartlett.

Ewing Marion Kauffman Foundation. (1999). *FastTrac new venture manual: making your entrepreneurial dream a reality*. Kansas City, MO: Author.

Luther, W. (2001). *The marketing plan: How to prepare and implement it*. (3rd ed.). New York: Amacom.

Middleton, R. (2003). A new marketing paradigm. *More Clients eZine*. Boulder Creek, CA: Action Plan Marketing.

TARP. (1999). Basic facts of customer compliant behavior and the impact of service on the bottom line. *Competitive Advantage*, 1-5.

Silbiger, S. (1999). *The ten-day MBA: A step-by-step guide to mastering the skills taught in America's top business schools*. (Rev.ed.). New York: Quill.

MARKETING

Chapter 9
Advocacy

Advocacy means acting in support of something. It is the process of marshalling information and resources to further a cause or bring about change. It may be change in our professional responsibilities, change for our clients in the services they receive, or change to the rules and regulations that govern our profession. Often people think of advocacy as the role of a professional lobbyist, but, in fact, we all use these skills on a daily basis to obtain what we want from others.

Advocacy involves everyone in an organization or profession. Each individual has a role to play and becomes vital in advocating for a desired outcome. Clinicians should be able to communicate the need for and benefits of service for individuals with speech-language and swallowing disorders. Speech-language pathologists (SLPs) should also be able to provide their clients with the tools to advocate for themselves, to empower them to ask for the services or coverage they need. Department heads, supervisors, and administrators may need to educate and organize their staffs to take action on issues that may impact their organization, profession, or the consumers they serve. As a speech-language pathologist, you should understand the most effective way to speak out for issues that affect you as an individual and as a part of a professional group.

Learning Outcomes

Describe the role advocacy plays in our individual and organizational lives.

Apply the advocacy process to your work setting.

Become involved in the legislative and regulatory process.

Chapter Focus

This chapter emphasizes the importance of advocacy by individuals and organizations to shape policies related to speech-language pathology. It focuses on understanding the **process of advocacy**, the **different types of advocacy**, the **value of networks and coalitions**, and **how the legislative and regulatory processes work**.

ADVOCACY

While the chapter focuses on larger efforts usually involving institutions, organizations, or grassroot networks, the principles of advocacy apply to individuals as well. The same multistep approach is useful for individuals looking to affect change in their professional situations.

The Basics of Advocacy

Advocacy efforts typically involve an organized approach to achieving change that benefits an individual, organization, profession, or consumer. The **stakeholder** of advocacy is the person, organization, or institution with a vested interest in the issue at hand. Stakeholders may include employees of a company, clients and consumers, organizations, or financial shareholders in a business venture. The **target audience** is the individual or group you want to influence. Targets may include decision makers in insurance companies, state and federal agencies, CEOs of companies, policymakers such as congressional representatives or state cabinet members, the media, special interest groups, and consumers.

The **process** of advocacy involves efforts such as –

- identifying issues,
- engaging individuals with similar interests in an issue to become "agents for change,"
- speaking in support of the issue in terms to which the target audience can relate,
- anticipating and addressing opposition to the issues successfully.

The **outcome** of advocacy involves creating change, either positive or negative, in the condition of an individual, organization, profession, or consumer group.

A speech-language pathologist may benefit from personal advocacy by receiving a promotion or salary increase. A client may benefit from a clinician's advocacy by having a procedure covered by insurance. An organization (such as a private practice) may benefit from regulatory advocacy through changes in the rules governing the setting where the services are being provided. The consumer might benefit from insurance advocacy through improved coverage for speech, language, hearing, and swallowing disorders.

Legislative advocacy can affect the professions of speech-language pathology and audiology by –

ADVOCACY

- introducing a new bill for speech and hearing services (e.g., mandating payment by insurance for services for all children within the state),

- amending an existing piece of legislation regarding speech and hearing (e.g., the legislation that links speech-language pathology to physical therapy and resulted in the $1500 cap being shared by SLP and PT, currently on hold),

- defeating a bill that would have been detrimental to the provision of speech and hearing services,

- enacting a new law or regulation beneficial to the profession and consumer groups (e.g., eligibility of SLPs to be assigned provider numbers so they can bill Medicare for services to Medicare beneficiaries)(ASHA, 2000).

Grassroots advocacy is a means of achieving a public policy goal through the combined lobbying efforts of a broad range of interested parties.

Advocacy is a multidirectional activity. While the SLP may be advocating to those in power for improvements in salary, the president of the organization may be advocating to employees to support changes in efficiency and productivity to support the viability of the organization. The middle manager, on the other hand, may need to advocate both to reporting employees as well as superiors to assure efficient operations. One of the most important aspects of advocacy, then, is to understand the universality and multidirectional aspects of advocacy.

The Value of Networks and Coalitions

An important part of advocacy is to leverage networks and coalitions. Networks are defined as "...an interconnected or interrelated chain, group, or system," whereas coalitions are "...a temporary alliance of distinct parties, persons, or states for a joint action" (Merriam-Webster, 2004). Developing networks or coalitions emphasizes the fact that no one person or organization is totally self-sufficient regarding the support or defeat of an advocacy issue. One of the most important aspects of developing networks and coalitions is to identify individuals and organizations that could successfully serve and contribute to the outcome of a goal. Considerable time and effort should be given to identifying the most appropriate contacts and to developing successful working relationships with those contacts. What is important is that the objectives of potential collaborators fit the overall mission of the network. The potential participant's responsibilities, motivation, ability to influence, and potential linkages to other groups should all be considered as well (ASHA, 2000).

Some networks or coalitions have a very short lifespan and are based on a specific issue. For example, a group of professional associations and industry groups formed a coalition to make public comments on the Centers for Medicare and Medicaid Services' regulation of the diagnoses that were considered appropriate for admission to inpatient rehabilitation facilities. Other coalitions of professional associations and consumer groups formed to advocate against the $1500 cap under Medicare Part B.

The National Insurance Advocacy Initiative (NIAI) is an example of a network of speech-language pathologists advocating for private insurance coverage reform. Originally formed in Ohio, the NIAI network expanded to include representatives from other states and to collaborate with ASHA to build on the knowledge and experience of its members.

In 2003, ASHA initiated a state-based reimbursement network to advocate for the equitable reimbursement and consistent coverage for communication services. The State Advocates for Reimbursement (STAR) network serves as a means to share and disseminate information regarding insurance negotiations. ASHA works with the STAR network by providing advocacy training information to members of the network, who then educate insurance companies, legislators, professionals, and consumers about the value of speech-language pathology and audiology services.

An example of a consumer and professional network is the ApraxiaKids network, which sponsors an e-mail group for parents and professionals to share clinical and insurance advocacy information. In this case, the network's focus is on a specific disorder (childhood apraxia) and the legislative, educational, and reimbursement issues surrounding it.

Networks are effective ways to monitor changes that may occur across a spectrum that is too broad for one individual to track. For example, a state speech-language pathology licensure law may be targeted for modification by a lobbying group (for example, by ENT physicians who oppose SLPs performing endoscopy). A network of SLPs throughout the U.S. can notify state associations and ASHA when changes to state licensure are being discussed so that a coordinated advocacy effort can take place.

Stakeholder Analysis

When undertaking advocacy activities, it is helpful to do a "stakeholder analysis." A stakeholder analysis begins with identifying the key individuals or groups who are either responsible for or have a vested interest in a given decision or action and their roles or relationships (Shortell & Kaluzny, 1994). These processes can be applied to **internal stakeholders** (such as supervisors or coworkers) or **external stakeholders** (such as parents or legislators). Stakeholder partnerships are a key strategy in advocacy and can be used to obtain a favorable decision on an issue that affects you personally or on an issue that affects groups on whose behalf you are working. In any stakeholder analysis, it is important to remember that stakeholders may be people who have vested interests and attitudes toward a change that are the opposite of your own.

ADVOCACY

Stakeholder Identification

It is important to identify each individual (or group) involved in a decision that will potentially affect a desired change, positively or negatively. To do that, we consider what the likelihood of benefit or harm will be to them as an effect of the decision. We also need to consider the relative amount of authority they have in making a decision. Stakeholder identification can include the following steps:

- Identify the people who are involved in making decisions that will affect or will be affected by a change (both negatively and positively).
- Rank each person as "positive," "neutral," or "negative" with regard to the likelihood of benefit from a change.
- Assess each person's degree of decision making power to implement or prevent a change.

Stakeholder Mapping

After you have identified your stakeholders, you can begin preparing an advocacy plan by considering who makes which decisions, what kind of information would be of interest to them, and how a decision could be presented to demonstrate a benefit to them. For example, if you were to advocate for lower productivity requirements or higher salaries for SLP staff, you would need to consider where the decision arenas are that affect those issues, who makes decisions in those arenas, and what the hierarchy of approvals would look like across the decision makers.

Decision Arena	Key Decision Makers				
	Facility Director	HR Benefits Office	Department Director	Department Business Officer	SLP Program Manager
Department budget	Approves	Recommends	Implements	Coordinates	Manages
Benefits package	Approves	Approves	Implements	Coordinates	Manages
Work schedule			Recommends	Recommends	Approves
Performance expectations			Recommends	Recommends	Approves

Issue-Specific Mapping

Another way to develop an advocacy strategy is to use issue-specific mapping, which is simply a graphic illustration of the major groups affected by an issue or decision and their relationships. This kind of graphic mapping allows you to consider who has the most direct role with decisions that affect the targeted issue, and more importantly, who has the most important indirect role by virtue of having a direct influence on those decision makers. Issue-specific mapping helps to

ADVOCACY

define a strategy for partnering with your stakeholders. Consider the example in Figure 9–1. The targeted issue is recognition of autism spectrum disorders as a medical condition to allow for earlier and better coverage for services to this population. The stakeholders include a variety of groups and individuals, with public policy makers and third-party payers playing a key role in the ultimate decisions and outcomes; however, these key decision makers are influenced by other groups, such as employers (who purchase employee coverage benefit plans) and members of the general and service provider public (parents, parent support groups, pediatricians, and "grassroots" SLPs and OTs, and their professional association affiliates), as well as the media, who are also positioned to influence decision makers about this issue.

Figure 9-1.
Issue-Specific Mapping on Autism Spectrum Disorders (ASD)

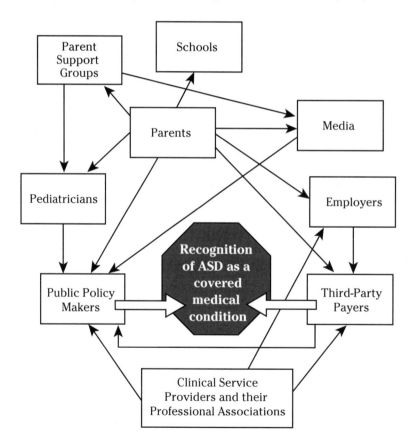

The Process of Advocacy

Advocacy is an organized, multistep process that involves developing a plan to reach a specific outcome. General planning involves having a clear understanding of your organization's strategic vision. Planning should include the development of action plans that support that vision. Long-range plans need to be developed and agreed upon by all participants. Then develop specific goals and objectives from the long-range plans. Compile resources to implement your objectives. Finally, establish timetables and strategies and review them to be sure they are realistic.

Identify the Outcome

The first step is to articulate a goal. What are you trying to accomplish? What is realistic? How will the results of your efforts impact those involved? What do you want to change? For example, are you trying to expand coverage levels or improve reimbursement rates? Are you seeking changes in the way your state licenses SLPs? Have a clear statement of what you hope to achieve.

Identify Your Target Audience

For advocacy to be successful, you need to understand your target audience. Whether you are advocating to your supervisor for a change in your work schedule, your department is seeking additional funds, or your organization is pushing a piece of legislation, you should know what and who influences the target audience. For example, if you want to adjust your schedule from five 8-hour days to four 10-hour days, you need to understand how that will affect your department as a whole. Why might your supervisor object? If your audience is an employer and you are asking for increased speech-language and hearing benefits, you'll want to know what is already included in the benefits package, the make-up of employees, and the additional cost to your employer for adding the coverage benefit.

If your organization is advocating for a piece of legislation to Congress, you should know to whom they listen now – constituents, lobbyists, the media, special interest groups, and other legislators. You should know the key players in their offices, their legislative records, what committees they serve on, what issues they have pursued in the past. Grassroots advocates in particular need to understand that they are one group of many seeking to advocate for their cause. (See also Grassroots Advocacy.)

Be specific in describing the target audience. Who are the individuals or organizations that you need to persuade? What are their interests? What are the

---

Examples of Outcomes

Keiko, the clinic manager, is constantly losing employees because there is a shortage of SLPs in her area, and the salary and benefits her clinic offers are not competitive. *She wants to increase the salary scale to retain employees.*

The major manufacturer in a small town does not cover speech-language and hearing benefits in its health benefits package. The local SLPs and parents who work at the company want *the manufacturer's benefits to cover speech-language and hearing services for children.*

The local school district typically hires Bachelor-level SLPs and has one ASHA-certified Master's-level SLP to "supervise" them. ASHA and the state association want the *district to offer a salary supplement to attract ASHA-certified SLPs.*

External Advocacy

Robert has a private speech-language pathology practice. One of the HMOs that he contracts with pays him a lower rate per session than Robert can afford to run his business. Robert schedules an appointment with the appropriate decision maker at the HMO and brings data to demonstrate the outcomes he has achieved with the HMO's clients in restoring functional communication and the average number of sessions it requires. He also brings the Medicare Physician Fee Schedule to show the rate of payment per CPT code for speech and swallowing. Robert must convince his **target audience**, the HMO contract manager, that his services are of high quality and value to the HMO, and therefore, they should pay a more competitive rate to retain his services.

arguments they might find most persuasive? How will supporting your cause affect them, either in a positive or negative way? It is important to understand your target audience's perspective.

Organize Networks and Coalitions

Identify and organize networks and/or coalitions to work toward the advocacy effort. What individuals or organizations have similar interests? What individuals are considered a respected source of support for your desired goal? What authorities support your cause? The goal here is to engage others with similar interests in the issue to become "agents of change."

Within smaller communities, SLPs can network by forming discussion or study groups as a way of connecting to other professionals who may have similar interests or work in similar settings. In a city that has several hospitals with SLP programs, the directors of those programs may decide to meet quarterly to discuss issues that affect them. They may decide to join together to advocate with their Medicare Fiscal Intermediary who has been denying services for dysphagia.

Individuals can join or form networks by attending local, state, and national meetings for speech-language pathologists and audiologists. By volunteering to participate in lobbying activities sponsored by those groups, they will come to know SLPs, lobbyists, and officials who have connections and interests in shared issues. Supported by the state speech-language and hearing association or ASHA, individuals can learn how to make "hill visits" to lobby their members of Congress on Capitol Hill or in their local districts on issues that affect them and their clients.

Communicate Your Message

Your message should summarize your issue. It should be short and to the point. Have facts available to support your position. This may include data on functional client outcomes that were achieved and the potential for reducing costs. Examples of ways that effective treatment can save costs include –

- reducing length of hospital or skilled nursing facility stay.
- increasing independence and thereby reducing costs for level of supervision and caregiving.
- eliminating tube feeding costs by returning patients to oral feeding.
- reducing risk of pneumonia, which requires costly treatment.
- comparing cost of treatment at different levels of care or by different providers.

ADVOCACY

- savings on costs to taxpayers for providing custodial care when students or clients could be mainstreamed or treated more efficiently.

If the information isn't already available, take the time to create it through research. The more factual your information, the better the chances are for a successful outcome.

How will you deliver your message? If you have developed a clear understanding of your target, you'll already have some idea of the most effective way to get your message across. Have a clear, cohesive message that everyone articulates. If you are organizing a letter-writing campaign, be sure to provide complete information about who to address and where to send the letter. Rather than using a form letter, provide the basic information that needs to be conveyed, and ask members to personalize their message. If you are meeting with targets in person, make sure your presentation is concise and to the point. Be ready to answer questions and counter opposing views. Stay on message and have materials available to leave with the target.

This is when negotiating skills are particularly useful. Many books have been written on influencing others (see Resources) but they share a common theme.

- **Separate the person from the problem**. For example, although you have not been successful in persuading your budget manager to fund a new position, you make an effort to maintain a pleasant personal relationship with her so that other requests you bring to her will not be negatively influenced by your unsuccessful negotiation.

- **Focus on interests, not positions**. For example, your state representative may be a fiscal conservative, but you lobby him to support additional funding for Medicaid in your state because you know that he has a child with a disability.

- **Consider options that will result in mutual gains**. Instead of competing with the director of OT/PT to get funding for new administrative positions, you may collaborate on a joint request demonstrating how you will share one new position.

- **Use objective criteria**. Rather than seeking to persuade a health plan to cover services for individuals with aphasia because it improves their quality of life, you demonstrate that the cost of caregiver support is decreased because your services train caregivers to communicate more effectively with the individuals.

Monitor and Evaluate Your Effort

It's important to keep track of how your effort is proceeding. This may be through e-mail updates to your coalition, teleconferencing, or meetings. Are coalition members contacting the right people? Be prepared to follow-up communications as needed, providing additional information to support your position.

You also need to evaluate your effort. Review what steps have been taken, how your presentation was received, and whether you met your objective. If you did not, what might help you be successful? Do you need to rethink your original goal? Do you need more data to support your argument, or do you need other people to support your effort?

Grassroots Advocacy

Grassroots advocacy is defined as "...the process of involving all individuals with a vested interest in a public policy goal to lobby with one voice in order to achieve a stated goal" (Ruder & Noplock, 2003).

The benefits of a grassroots effort include an increased commitment to the goal, shared ownership, knowledge about the issue, and a better chance at success. Being an advocate at the legislative level can be rewarding but frustrating. One of the biggest challenges is to understand fully how the system works–how legislative and regulatory changes are made.

Understanding the legislative and regulatory processes

To effect change in laws or rules, advocates need to have a clear understanding of the legislative and regulatory processes. Legislative advocacy is designed to influence the legislative process. This may be introducing, amending, or defeating a bill or ensuring that a bill is enacted into law at the state or federal level. Regulatory advocacy is designed to influence government agencies that are responsible for implementing regulations from enacted legislation. Regulatory advocacy is useful in influencing the interpretation and enforcement of regulations. Both forms of advocacy may occur at the local, state, or federal level.

Federal legislative activities result from actions of Congress. ASHA's public policy agenda has included goals such as advocating for legislation to allow direct billing by SLPs under Medicare or to repeal the $1,500 therapy cap under the Medicare Part B outpatient program. Federal regulatory activities occur within departments such as the U.S. Department of Health and Human Services, Food and Drug Administration (FDA), Occupational Safety and Health Administration (OSHA), and the Department of Education. For example, the prospective payments systems developed by the Centers for Medicare and Medicaid Services (CMS, part of the Department of Health and Human Services) are examples of regulations developed in response to federal legislation mandating a reduction in health care costs (i.e., the Balanced Budget Act of 1997).

State legislative activities result from actions by state legislatures. An example of state legislation advocacy would be to facilitate the introduction of a bill mandating that health care plans include a benefit option for speech, language, swallowing, hearing, or hearing aid benefits, including children with genetic or congenital disorders (see the Case Study, **Expanding Coverage Options**). State legislative processes will vary from state-to-state.

State regulatory activities occur in state departments, such as those that regulate health, education, or business. One example of state regulatory activity is the state licensure laws. Each state has its own regulations regarding licensing for speech-language professionals. ASHA has compiled *State Regulation of Audiology and Speech-Language Pathology*, a listing of the licensure requirements for each state (see Resources). An example of local legislative and regulatory activities would be local school district regulations. These regulations are typically located in the county education department (ASHA, 2000).

There are numerous publications and Web sites that provide detailed instructions on how the legislative process works (see Resources) but here is a quick overview.

Steps in the Federal Legislative Process
1. **Introduce the bill in the House or Senate**. The bill is referred to committee(s) and or subcommittee(s) for consideration (e.g., House Committee on Ways and Means; House Committee on Ways and Means, Subcommittee on Health).

2. **Hold hearings on the proposed bill**. Individuals and organizations may testify or be called as witnesses to support or oppose the bill. Subcommittee makes changes (mark-ups) to the bill. Bill dies in committee or is passed and referred to full House or Senate.

3. **Passage by both House and Senate (it may become part of a larger omnibus bill)**. A joint committee may be formed to resolve differences in versions of the bill.

4. **If the bill is passed by both bodies, the President signs or vetoes it**.

Although these steps appear simple, getting through each step may involve a long and complex process. An initiative can die at any stage, and it can take years of persistence to accomplish your goal. Legislation must survive numerous votes before final passage, and there are numerous places a bill can get bogged down. For advocates who want to influence a particular piece of legislation, either to support or oppose it, grassroots efforts early on are critical.

Federal Regulatory Process
Regulations are the rules that set out how laws will be implemented. They also describe how an agency or department will fulfill its goals and objectives. Once a piece of legislation has passed Congress and been signed by the President, it is up to the appropriate federal agency to develop regulations that establish how the

ADVOCACY

law is carried out. While laws are generally broad in nature, regulations are more specific. For example, the Balanced Budget Act of 1997 mandated the implementation of new regulations to contain health care costs for Medicare beneficiaries. Over the next 5 years, the Health Care Financing Administration (now called the Centers for Medicare and Medicaid Services) developed regulations to implement different prospective payment systems for skilled nursing facilities, inpatient rehabilitation facilities, and home health agencies.

Proposed regulations and amendments to existing regulations must be listed in the *Federal Register* at least 30 days before they are to take effect. The public must be allowed time to comment, suggest changes, or object to the regulation. In some cases, public hearings are held.

How Grassroots Advocacy Works

The multistep process of advocacy outlined earlier applies at the grassroots level as well. It is particularly critical to understand your audience, since in many cases you will be targeting legislators or government officials.

Government officials and lawmakers may be influenced by the media, colleagues, their staff, lobbyists, and special interest groups. Constituents are also important in influencing legislators. "Constituents play a critical role in the legislative process by acting as a conduit of information between elected officials and their home districts" (ASHA, 2002, p. 1).

Because the grassroots advocate is one of many people supporting an issue, he or she needs to be prepared when dealing with legislators. The advocate needs to have a strong understanding of the lawmaker, including his or her legislative record, affiliations, philosophy, and committee work. Additional information on communicating your message can be found under Resources, but ASHA recommends the following for effective meetings with legislators:

- Explain who you are and why you want to meet with the representative when you call to make your appointment.
- Be on time and be prepared to wait.
- Get to the point quickly and be clear about what you want.
- Keep your message focused. Request a specific action.
- Be polite.
- Have materials ready to leave at the end of the meeting.
- Send thank you letters to the legislator after your meeting, reiterating your message and including any additional information.

Summary

While speaking out for your interests and issues may seem overwhelming, it is only through advocacy that changes take place. Every professional should be aware and involved in advocacy efforts at the individual, institutional, and governmental levels. It is only through coordinated efforts that we can achieve meaningful changes and have an impact on the growth of our profession and the satisfaction of our many stakeholders.

References

American Speech-Language-Hearing Association. (2000). *Curriculum guide to grassroots advocacy in speech-language pathology and audiology*. Rockville, MD: Author.

American Speech-Language-Hearing Association. (2002). *Advocacy training manual*. Washington, D.C: Soap Box Consulting.

Merriam-Webster Online. Retrieved June 25, 2004, from http://www.m-w.com.

Ruder, K., & Noplock, M. (2003). Grassroots legislative advocacy. *Perspectives on Administration and Supervision, 13(2)*, 4-6.

Shortell, S.M., & Kaluzny, A.D. (1994). *Health care management: organization design and behavior*. (3rd ed.). Albany, NY: Delmar Publishers, Inc. (4th ed., 1999).

ADVOCACY

Case Study #1

Productivity and Performance: The Busy Clinician

Carolyn is the manager of an outpatient rehab department of a small, suburban hospital. Her unit employs one full-time speech-language pathologist (SLP), five physical therapists (PTs), and three occupational therapists (OTs) and receives a steady stream of referrals from its inpatient program such that there is usually a waiting list for services. Jessie, the SLP, sometimes lets her treatment sessions run overtime, leaving little time to talk to families at the close of sessions. As a result, Jessie spends several hours a week talking to family members on the phone. She stays late several hours a week to write lengthy diagnostic and therapy reports, but despite her efforts, her reports are frequently overdue. Occasionally, missing documentation has resulted in delayed payments and insurance denials.

As the only SLP, Jessie is a member of several client care teams and is also active in hospital committees, including the community outreach committee. She works enthusiastically and tirelessly to organize the hospital staff to volunteer for health fairs and community projects several weekends a year. Jessie is described by clients and staff as "bright," "caring," "dedicated." Her coworkers also describe her as "busy" and "overworked;" however, her monthly clinical productivity has consistently averaged less than 45%.

When Carolyn has attempted to talk to Jessie about managing her productivity and reducing the delays in documentation, Jessie has responded by saying that she is so far behind she can't possibly add any more client care time to her schedule and that she is doing her best to provide quality services to her clients. She points out that she enjoys doing the committee projects, and she feels she is contributing to staff morale. She says that her productivity as the SLP cannot be expected to be the same as PTs and OTs, as communication goals are far more complicated to manage than the OT and PT goals and more challenging to document adequately. She also points out that she is the last one out of the building every day, frequently taking work home. Jessie complains that, even though she has not met her productivity targets, her caseload has become unmanageable and involves cases with problems that demand her time and often exceed her expertise. She is developing tension headaches nearly every afternoon. What can Jessie's manager, Carolyn, do to help a busy clinician become an efficient clinician?

Carolyn identifies Jessie's problems as –

- having difficulty managing work time;
- holding unrealistic and unclear job expectations;
- lacking knowledge and skills for working with difficult clients;
- feeling powerless and like a victim.

Performance Improvement Objective 1: Understanding and Empowerment

Carolyn sets up a meeting with Jessie to review the problems and the impact on Jessie's health. She praises Jessie for her excellent work ethic, the quality of her work, and contributions to the program. But she explains that she and Jessie need to work together to find ways to help manage work time more efficiently, clarify job expectations, and work within her scope of practice, knowledge, and skills as a SLP. Carolyn empowers Jessie to create a manageable action plan that puts effort into the areas that benefit the client, the program, and herself. They agree that they need to work together to find a balance of client care and service activities and to look for ways to improve efficiencies.

Performance Improvement Objective 2: Productivity

Carolyn explains how the department budget works, including personnel costs and overhead, how productivity targets for each clinician are determined, and how the average ratio of charges billed versus payments collected for speech-language pathology procedures is a factor in determining the productivity targets. Carolyn asks Jessie to look at how she is spending her day and how that is affecting the time available for direct client care. They discuss the importance of placing direct client care, documentation, case management, and team meetings ahead of service activities. They decide to restrict Jessie's availability for community outreach meetings to early and later times of the day when clients are not typically scheduled. They agree to work together to simplify and prioritize tasks and to reduce the paperwork burden only to the essential requirements. They discuss the importance of timely documentation to ensure the best return on efforts. Carolyn points out that to cover just the salary costs of Jessie's position, given an average collection rate of only 62% of billed services, Jessie will need to increase her current average productivity by at least 12% - 15%.

Performance Improvement Objective 3: Time Management

Jessie agrees to end her sessions at 50 minutes and use the remaining 10 minutes to talk with families and document the session. Jessie and Carolyn agree to work immediately toward streamlining all documentation and using simplified, electronic records for all of the therapy services wherever possible. They also discuss how to respond politely to families' and clients' demands and to discourage phone calls after work. Jessie and Carolyn design a set daily schedule for Jessie to follow during the upcoming month and determine an interim productivity goal.

Performance Improvement Objective 4: Knowledge and Skills

They discuss what counseling services are part of the professional services provided by SLPs and how to schedule and charge for those sessions. They discuss the concerns that necessitate referrals to other professionals or community social work services. Jessie identifies areas in which she would like to increase her knowledge to work more effectively with clients. They agree to meet each week for the next 8 weeks to review how these strategies have worked.

Case Study #2

Molly's Private Practice: The ABCs of Accounting

Molly leaves her job to start her own practice. The following is an illustration of her business activity for her first month, and more importantly, how she accounts for it.

- Molly takes $7,000 of her savings and uses it as capital to start her business. This $7,000 represents her equity.
- Molly buys therapy materials, tests, and office furniture for $2,500 on account.
- Molly provides therapy services to Client A totaling $1,000, billed to insurance.
- Molly provides therapy services to Client B totaling $800, paid in cash.
- Molly spends $100 cash on an ad in her community newsletter.

The first thing that Molly needs to do is to set up her various accounts that will be used over time to record her business transactions. Molly sets up the following accounts:

- Cash
- Accounts Receivable
- Accounts Payable
- Property
- Equity
- Revenue
- Expense

The first five accounts are used for her balance sheet and the last two are used on her income statement. Molly would do well to categorize her expenses further for tracking purposes (e.g., materials, supplies, marketing, utilities).

Debits and Credits

Few accounting concepts create more confusion that debits and credits. Debits and credits are used to make sure all transactions balance and are the cornerstone of double entry or "T" accounting.

Note: This is not intended to be accounting advice or a recommendation of how to organize your accounts. The best advice for any situation will come from your own accountant.

Rather than thinking of debits or credits as increases or decreases, think of them in terms of entries made on the left or right hand side of a T. Debits go on the left and credits go on the right. On a balance sheet, debits, or left side balances, include assets, and credits (on the right) include liabilities and equity. On an income statement, debits include expenses and credits include revenue.

Type of Statement	Debit	Credit
Balance Sheet	Assets	Liabilities & Equity
Income Statement	Expense	Revenue

There are two places where transactions will appear before they show up on any financial statement. The first is the **general journal**, which is a running tally of transactions. Each transaction recorded in the general journal must be "balanced." That is, each transaction must debit at least one account and credit at least one other, and the sum of the debits must equal the sum of the credits. This is where the term "balancing the books" comes from. Each and every transaction impacts at least two accounts, based on the scheme described above.

Based on the simple activity from Molly's first month, the general journal would look like this:

			Debit	Credit
1. Debit	Cash		$7000	
	Credit	Equity		$7000

The first entry shows that Molly took $7,000 of her own money to start her business, so the $7,000 needs to appear as a debit to cash, which is an asset, and as a credit to equity. This entry increases the balances in both the Cash and the Equity accounts.

			Debit	Credit
2. Debit	Property		$1000	
Debit	Expenses		$1800	
	Credit	Accounts Payable		$2800

Entry #2 shows that Molly acquired furniture costing $1,000, which is debited to property because it is an asset. She also bought therapy materials and supplies costing $1,800, which is debited to expenses. She paid by credit card, so she balances this transaction by crediting accounts payable, or A/P, which is a liability.

This entry increases the balances in the Property, Accounts Payable, and Expense accounts.

		Debit	Credit
3. Debit	Accounts Receivable	$1000	
Credit	Revenue		$1000

Entry #3 shows that Molly generated $1,000 by performing services and billed the insurance company. Accounts receivable (A/R) is an asset, so she debits A/R and credits revenue. This entry increases the balances in both the Accounts Receivable and Revenue accounts.

		Debit	Credit
4 Debit	Cash	$800	
Credit	Revenue		$800

Entry #4 shows that Molly generated $800 for clinical services paid in cash. Cash is an asset, so it is debited, and revenue is credited. This entry increases the balances in both the Cash and Revenue accounts.

		Debit	Credit
5. Debit	Expense	$100	
Credit	Cash		$100

Entry #5 shows that Molly paid $100 in cash for an ad in her community paper. She credits her cash account while debiting her expenses. This entry increases the balance in the Expense account and decreases the balance in the Cash account.

Next, Molly's activities would be recorded in the **general ledger**, which contains each account in the form of a "T," with debits on the left and credits on the right. The general journal is a running list of all transactions with one account debited and one account credited. The general ledger is a listing of all transactions within each account.

General Journal describes activity at the transaction level.

General Ledger describes activity at the account level.

Molly's general ledger for her first month's activities would look like the following. Remember that the general ledger condenses each transaction to the account level. Each account is represented as a "T" with debits on the left and credits on the right.

These accounts will appear on the Balance sheet.

```
        Cash
   7000  |  100
    800  |
```

```
         A/R
   1000  |
         |
```

```
      Property
   1000  |
         |
```

```
         A/P
         |  2800
         |
```

```
       Equity
         |  7000
         |
```

These accounts will appear on the Income Statement.

```
       Revenue
         |  1000
         |   800
```

```
       Expense
   1000  |
    800  |
```

The next step in setting up Molly's books is to create her **trial balance**, which is a summary of the final balance in each account after a given period. Each account will only have a credit or a debit balance since the debit and credit columns are totaled and the credits are subtracted from the debits. This would be the case in any account for which there were entries on both sides. Using the general ledger balances above, the following totals are calculated:

Molly's Trial Balance

Account	Debit	Credit
Cash	7700	
Accounts Receivable	1000	
Property	1000	
Accounts Payable		2800
Equity		7000
Revenue		1800
Expense	1900	
Totals	11600	11600

The Income Statement

The income statement can be represented by the following equation:

Net Income = Revenue – Expense

From the trial balance, Molly can create her various financial statements. Based on the trial balance, taking the revenue and expense accounts, the income statement appears as follows:

Revenue	$1,800
Expense	1,900
Net Income (loss)	($ 100)

The above income statement does not show any categories in revenue or expense. Categorizing these totals will help in assessing performance, tracking trends, and analyzing budget variance. This is where accounting software is critical. A more detailed income statement for the same activity may look something like Figure 1.

This income statement was generated using the accrual-based method of accounting, which records income when earned and expense when incurred. Note that all revenue and expense transactions from the general journal are reflected here.

Figure 1.
Accrual-Based Income Statement

Revenue		
Therapy Services	$1,800	
Evaluation Services		—
Total Revenue		1,800
Expenses		
Supplies	500	
Advertising	100	
Test Materials	400	
Therapy Materials	900	
Total Expenses		1,900
Net Income (Loss)		**$ (100)**

Molly could choose to list her revenue by referral source, payment type, or population. The therapy and evaluation categories are completely arbitrary.

An alternative format is shown in Figure 2. This income statement was generated using the cash-basis method of accounting, which records income and expense when money changes hands. Note that only cash transactions from the general journal are reflected here. Since only cash transactions are reflected, this can also be used as a statement of cash flow.

Figure 2.
Cash-Basis Income Statement

Revenue		
Therapy Services	$800	
Evaluation Services		—
Total Revenue		800
Expenses		
Supplies		—
Advertising	100	
Supplies		
Therapy Materials		—
Total Expenses		100
Net Income (Loss)		**$ 700**

Using the cash-basis method, Molly shows a $700 profit, but using the accrual-basis method, she shows a $100 loss on the exact same business activity. The difference is in the way it is accounted for. With the exception of some very small businesses, the accrual method is generally considered a more accurate description of a business' operations. It matches income earned in any period to the expenses incurred to generate that revenue in that same period.

The "bottom line," or Net Income (Loss) from an income statement is combined with the net income (or losses) from all previous years and is represented in the balance sheet as retained earnings. This shows the cumulative net gain (or loss) generated by the entity. If the owner took money out of the company for personal use, this is called owner's draft, and it reduces either equity or retained earnings, depending on circumstances.

The Balance Sheet

The balance sheet can be represented by the following equation:

Assets = Liabilities + Equity

Based on the trial balance, Molly's balance sheet after her first month would look like this:

Assets

Cash	$7,700
Accounts Receivable	1,000
Property	1,000
Total Assets	$9,700

Liabilities

Accounts Payable	$2,800
Equity	7,000
Retained Earnings	(100)
Total Liabilities and Equity	9,700

As you can see, the total assets equal the sum of liabilities, equity, and retained earnings. Hence, the term **balance sheet**.

As Molly's practice expands, she may want to purchase equipment such as a computer or fax machine. She can depreciate durable equipment that will be used to generate revenue over a period of time. If she spends $2,000 on computer equipment, she can allocate that amount over 3 years on her income statement as depreciation expense and on her balance sheet as accumulated depreciation because the computer equipment will be used in her work for at least that long, not just during her first month.

Molly, like most start-up business owners, did not take any money for herself in the first month. Rather she kept income as retained earnings, which was re-invested in her business and added to her equity the following month. When she does begin taking money, it will be considered Owner's Draw and will decrease her equity.

Case Study #3

Improving Departmental Performance: Good, Better, Best

The Speech-Language Pathology Department at "We're the Best" Hospital had ongoing monitors of its no shows and waiting list times as quality indicators. The data indicated a consistent no show and cancellation percentage for initial speech-language diagnostic evaluations of 35% over two consecutive quarters. Since evaluations were scheduled for 3-hour blocks of time, this affected clinician productivity and satisfaction (as annual pay increases were based on productivity). Client satisfaction also suffered. Clients who waited for several weeks to be scheduled continued to wait to be seen, despite potential openings.

The department's performance improvement team decided to study the problem. The team took a Plan-Do-Check-Act approach to problem solving. They looked at the typical experience at similar facilities (i.e., benchmarks) in the professional community and considered models for scheduling that are used in other industries. The team also conducted a time study, which revealed that only 1 in 8 evaluations took the full 3 hours, but 7 of 8 took 90 minutes or less. Based on this information, the team developed the following plan:

- Evaluations would be overbooked by 35%, based on the average show rate.

- Scheduling would be in a "staggered clinic" format, where the clients and parents were informed that there may be up to a 30-minute wait.

- Clients would not be assigned to a specific speech-language pathologist (SLP), but evaluations would be conducted by the next available clinician.

- Evaluations for similar or less complicated problems would be scheduled on the same morning, and several SLPs would participate in the diagnostic clinic as a diagnostic team.

- Clinicians were encouraged to consult with one another, if needed, for more difficult or puzzling cases.

Using this model, five SLPs were scheduled for 15 evaluations in a morning. The evaluations were scheduled for either an 8:30 a.m. or 10:00 a.m. time slot. Assuming a 35% no-show rate, this model predicted that, on average, only 10 clients would come, so there was fairly good assurance that each SLP would do at least 2 evaluations in a morning. Although some evaluations might require 2 or 3 hours, most could be scheduled to be completed in 90 minutes. After implementing the staggered clinic schedule model, the team continued to collect data to check the effects of this change (waiting list numbers and wait times; number of diagnostic procedures billed per week; billed time versus worked time for clinicians assigned to the clinic; client satisfaction survey data; and staff satisfaction survey data).

Ultimately, the team found the following:

- Decreased numbers of clients on the waiting list and quicker referral to intake time because more clients could be scheduled.
- Increased revenue.
- Higher productivity for the staff.
- Improved client satisfaction scores.
- High staff satisfaction.
- Additional "quality dividends"; clinicians reported the quality of their diagnostic assessments had improved because this new clinic model allowed staff members to collaborate more easily on difficult cases. Surprisingly, the no-show percentage actually decreased, possibly because clients were getting scheduled closer to the time when the initial referral was made, when the parent's concerns were most acute.

A report of the outcome of the study was prepared and disseminated by the team.

Case Study #4

Expanding Coverage Options: A Grassroots Effort in Florida

A grassroots effort was organized by members of the Florida Speech-Language-Hearing Association to promote legislation that would mandate coverage for speech, language, swallowing, hearing, or hearing aid benefits. Many health care plans do not include this coverage, and policyholders frequently don't know this option might be available for an additional, nominal premium.

The Governor's Office had already made it known that mandating coverage would not be acceptable to the governor and would result in a veto. An alternative plan was to introduce a bill or amendment that could mandate the *option* of coverage for an additional premium.

To decrease publicity for the Governor's position and increase chances of success, the negotiating team decided to attach an amendment to a bill on increasing health care access, which is typically introduced in the Legislature. The team also decided to include genetic or congenital etiologies in this amendment as this population was frequently excluded from existing policies.

The team needed to define the "level of benefits" being requested prior to the construction of the amendment, particularly because genetic or congenital disorders can potentially be complex and extensive. The negotiating team decided to use the level of benefits with the terminology noted in the Florida Medicaid handbook for both therapy and hearing because the Medicaid handbook was an approved government document.

Analysis of the Opposition

The executive branch of the government had indicated it would approve the amendment if it did not mandate coverage but merely mandated the option of coverage for an additional premium. However, insurance companies in the state were opposed. Negotiations with the insurance companies took place over several days. During negotiations, the key question was: "Does this suggested change by the insurance companies substantially alter the major thrust of this amendment?" As long as the suggested change kept the major focus of the amendment intact, the alterations were accepted by the negotiating team.

The team worked closely with a paid legislative lobbyist who was instrumental in "opening doors" and briefing the team on "do's and don'ts" during the legislative visits. The lobbyist reviewed the political party, interests, voting history, and potential support for this amendment prior to the visit with each legislator. He also provided constructive review and suggestions after each visit. His considerable expertise in the legislative process was instrumental in moving this amendment through the process.

The amendment was successfully attached to a health access bill. The bill and amendment successfully passed the Florida House Health Care Committee, the Florida Senate Committee, and the first two readings on the Floor. But the Legislature ran out of time prior to the third (formal only) reading, and the bill was not voted on during that session.

Follow Up Activities

Members of the negotiating team followed up with the sponsor of the legislation and thanked him for his support. They also asked that the amendment be reintroduced on the health access bill when the legislation is reintroduced during the general session. The sponsor of the bill indicated his willingness to reintroduce the bill with the proposed amendment during the next general session. Although the bill and amendment had support for passage at this time, the sponsor cautioned that the group needed to continue lobbying for this amendment the second time around in the event that opponents to a bill would resurface and reorganize.

The team engaged in the following activities:

- Attended county legislative meetings and presented a plan to secure support.
- Sent a letter to legislators requesting support for the legislation.
- Sent a thank-you note to legislators that responded.
- Called members of the state association to ask them to meet with legislators in each district to ask for their support.

The state association also conducted a series of informational workshops around the state with state association members. All participants received a list of their legislators, the issue at hand, a sample letter to their legislator, the legislative proposal, and an advocacy sheet for parents.

Appendix A

Example of Chair and Member Responsibilities

Chairpersons

- Define and delineate the charter, purpose, or mission statement for the committee.
- Define responsibilities (committee chairperson, members).
- Establish the meeting time and place.
- Develop a communication plan (e.g., e-mail distribution list).
- Prepare and disseminate the meeting agenda before meetings.
- Disseminate relevant background information to committee members.
- Conduct meetings.
- Start and end the meetings on time.
- Ensure minutes are kept and distributed.
- Make sure all members actively participate and are heard by others.
- Review at staff meetings, or send a brief summary of committee activities to the staff newsletter.

Members

- Attend all meetings.
- Notify the chair if you need to miss the meeting.
- Arrive at meetings on time.
- Participate in discussions and complete assigned or delegated tasks and projects.
- Listen to and respect the opinions and ideas of others.

Appendix B

Tips for Leading Committees or Teams

Agree on the mission or goals

- Define the objectives and purpose.
- Achieve agreement on appropriate outcomes and indicators of success.

Assign members

- Make sure you have the right people on the team, those who have the knowledge and skills to accomplish the task.
- Ask only relevant people to meetings to keep numbers down.
- Allow staff to decline if they feel they have nothing to contribute or are not interested.

Determine roles

- Assign roles to members. Roles should be matched to personality and strengths.
- Make sure team members have knowledge, resources, training, and skills.
- Balance the team with personality types and strengths.
- Define clearly the responsibilities and expectations of each member. Make every member accountable.

Clarify expectations

- Inform team of how much autonomy and decision-making power will be allowed before asking for feedback or approval.
- When needed, encourage brainstorming without judgment. Then have the team vote to narrow down the ideas.
- Encourage collaboration and cooperation, not competition.
- Monitor and document progress regularly through written minutes and meetings with the leader.
- Reward team efforts, not individual efforts.

Set timelines

- Establish deadlines to accomplish tasks.
- Keep meetings to the shortest amount of time to cover the agenda.

Manage the meetings

- Distribute agenda, minutes, and relevant documents before meetings.
- Plan on what needs to be accomplished by the end of each meeting.
- When appropriate, use organized brainstorming.
- Encourage all members to participate.
- Be an active listener.
- Use meeting time to discuss and plan; implement the plans outside the meeting.
- Assign tasks and responsibilities to be completed by the next meeting.

Monitor performance

- Review progress and timeline for projects on a regular basis.
- Revise plans accordingly.

Appendix C

Tips for Efficient Use of Time

Delegate nontechnical tasks. Consider all the tasks you perform that are and are not clinical (copying, filing, making materials, faxing, transporting patients, etc.). Brainstorm with other staff or your supervisor as to how the nontechnical, administrative tasks can be handled more efficiently by existing or volunteer support personnel. For example, recruit undergraduate SLP student interns, ask for parent or family volunteers, partner with another department for more support staff, or develop a proposal for your own support staff person, based on the amount of licensed staff time saved and available for more productive activities.

Streamline, minimize, and automate documentation. Redesign your documentation to use templates or electronic formats as much as possible; plan for at least 10 minutes of documentation time between clients, and try to limit documentation to that time frame.

Reduce no shows and cancellations. Develop waiting lists to fill in for cancellations; utilize client attendance contracts; develop a reminder call system for upcoming appointments; schedule clients in small groups, if appropriate.

Conduct a work flow analysis. List the sequence of tasks involved in achieving a particular objective, who did each task, how long it took to complete, and whether that task added any value to the objective–was that step needed? Then, eliminate all unnecessary tasks, reassign all clerical tasks to support staff (and to patients and families, when appropriate), and automate wherever possible.

Set benchmarks. Establish outcome criteria, or benchmarks, based on your own standards or those of comparison groups for service delivery quality, time, or payment targets (number of claim denials, patient satisfaction ratings, time between intake to scheduling, duration of time clients spend on the waiting list for therapy, number of trips to the ward required to complete an inpatient consultation, time required to obtain an AAC device, etc.).

Consider flexible scheduling. If flexible scheduling is an alternative, take advantage of high demand times for scheduling patients. For example, clinicians who work with older children with special needs in an outpatient clinic may be better able to maintain productivity if these children are scheduled between 10:00 a.m. – 6:30 p.m., allowing for more time after school in the afternoons. Hospital-based clinicians may be able to schedule patient care team or staff meetings at 7:30 a.m. when patients on the wards are not usually available.

Schedule administrative time. Schedule nonbillable, administrative time into some part of your day or week; build time in your schedule for lunch and mental breaks. The occasional "brown bag" staff meeting is unavoidable, but routinely working through the lunch hour or failing to take short breaks between clients is not conducive to efficiency.

Appendix D

Community Clinic Service Agreement

Client: _____ Birthday: _____

Agency/School Requesting Services: _____

Representative/Contact: _____ Title: _____

Phone: _____ Fax: _____

Address: _____

_____

Services Requested

___ SLP Group ___ @ _____ /Session

     and/or ___ Individual Therapy @ _____ /Session

___ SLP/Deaf Educator Team Group Therapy @ _____ /Session

___ Audiologic Assessment

___ Teacher/Staff Inservices @ _____ /Session

___ Parent Training @ _____ /Session

___ Travel @ _____ /mile

___ Materials @ cost

Team: _____ **Lead Clinician:** _____

Inclusive Dates of Services: Starting _____ **Ending** _____

Total Number of _____ **Minute Evaluation Sessions:** _____

Total Number of _____ **Minute Treatment Sessions:** _____

Total Number of _____ **Minute Inservice/Counseling/Training**

     Other Sessions: _____

Equipment (describe): _____

Signatures: _____   _____

       Clinic Manager or Representative   **Date**

       _____   _____

      Agency/School Representative   **Date**

Source: Pediatric Speech-Language Pathology Programs; Vanderbilt Bill Wilkerson Center, Department of Hearing and Speech Sciences.

Appendix E

Model Superbill for Speech-Language Pathology

The following is a model of a superbill that could be used by a speech-language pathology practice when billing private health plans. This sample is not meant to dictate which services should or should not be listed on the bill. Most billable codes are from the American Medical Association (AMA) Current Procedural Terminology (CPT)© 2003. Prosthetic and durable medical equipment codes, such as speech generating device codes, are published by the Centers for Medicaid and Medicare (CMS) as Healthcare Common Procedure Codes.

The superbill is a standard form that health plans use to process claims. For the professional rendering services, it provides a time efficient means to document services, fees, codes, and other information required by insurance companies (i.e., certification and licensure). The patient uses this form to file for health plan payment.

NOTE: *This is only a model. Therefore some procedures, codes, or other pertinent information may have changed or may not be found in the following model. For a complete list of CPT and ICD-9 codes, the ASHA Health Plan Coding & Claims Guide is available through ASHA's Web site or by calling ASHA's Product Sales at 1-888-498-6699.*

Model Superbill for Speech-Language Pathology

Patient: _____ Insured: _____

Referring Physician: _____ Address: _____

File: _____ Insurance Plan: _____

Date: _____ Insurance Plan #: _____

Date Initial Symptom: _____ Date First Consultation: _____

Place of Service: ___ Home ___ Office ___ Other

Diagnosis:

Primary (Medical) _____ **ICD-9 code** _____

Secondary (Speech-language pathology) _____ **ICD-9 code** _____

Services:

CPT	Procedure	Charge	CPT	Procedure	Charge
Swallowing Function			*Speech and Language*		
92526	Treatment of swallowing dysfunction and/or oral function for feeding		92506	Evaluation of speech, language, voice, communication, auditory processing, and/or aural rehabilitation status	
92610	Evaluation of swallowing function		92507	Treatment of speech, language, voice, communication, auditory processing disorder (includes aural Rehabilitation), individual	
92611	Motion fluoroscopic evaluation of swallowing function				
92612	Flexible fiberoptic endoscopic evaluation of swallowing				
92613	with physician interpretation and report		92508	group, two or more individuals	
92614	Laryngeal sensory test		97532	Development of cognitive skills to improve attention, memory, problem solving, direct one-on-one patient contact by the provider	
92615	with physician interpretation and report				
92616	Flexible fiberoptic endoscopic evaluation of swallowing and laryngeal sensory testing		97533	Sensory integrative techniques to enhance sensory processing and promote adaptive responses to environmental demands	
92617	with physician interpretation and report				

CPT	Procedure	Charge
92511	Nasopharyngoscopy w/ endoscope	
92520	Laryngeal function studies	
96105	Assessment of aphasia	
96110	Developmental testing; limited, w/ interpretation and report	
96111	Extended, with interpretation and report, per hour	
96115	Neurobehavioral status exam, w/ interpretation and report, per hour	
31575	Laryngoscopy; flexible fiberoptic; diagnostic	
31579	Laryngoscopy; flexible or rigid fiberoptic, with stroboscopy	

Augmentative and Alternative Communication

CPT	Procedure	Charge
92597	Evaluation for use/ fitting of voice prosthetic	
92605	Evaluation for prescription of non-speech generating augmentative and alternative communication device	

CPT	Procedure	Charge
92606	Therapeutic service(s) for the use of non-speech generating augmentative and alternative communication device, including programming and modification	
92607	Evaluation for prescription for speech-generating augmentative and alternative communication device; face-to-face with the patient; evaluation, first hour	
92608	Evaluation for speech device; each additional 30 minutes	
92609	Therapeutic services for the use of speech-generating device, including programming and modification	
V5336	Repair/Modification of AAC device (excluding adaptive hearing aid)	

Other Procedures

CPT	Procedure	Charge
92700	Otorhinolaryngological service or procedure	
Total Charges		

I hereby authorize direct payment of benefits to Speech Services, Inc.

Signature: _____

I hereby authorize Irene Smith, MA, CCC-SLP to release any information acquired in the course of treatment.

Signature: _____

Irene Smith, MA, CCC-SLP
Speech Services, Inc.
555 Anywhere Road
Anywhere, CA 55555
(555) 555-5555
SS #000-00-0000
Tax ID #00-00000
California License #0000
Speech-Language Pathology

Source: American Speech-Language-Hearing Association, Rockville, MD.

Appendix F

Justification for Treatment

Sample Letter

Date

XYZ Health Plan
500 Main Street, Suite 101
Washington, DC 20011

> Re: Adam Wilson
> Member ID#: 321654789
> Group Name: VWXY
> Group ID#: 2500

Dear Claims Department:

I am writing in support of payment by XYZ Federal Employee Program (XYZ FEP) for speech-language pathology services provided to Adam Wilson. Speech-language pathology treatment is medically necessary to treat Adam's speech-language deficits associated with autism. Autism is a neurobiological disorder severely impairing the individual's ability to process and integrate information from the environment. Communication impairments associated with autism are well recognized. Barry Prizant, PhD, in the chapter on Communication Problems in the Autistic Client, states:

> *Speech, language, and communication problems are pervasive in autism spectrum disorders. These problems are apparent in verbal and nonverbal behavior, prelinguistic and linguistic communication, and in other receptive and expressive modalities (Prizant, B., 1998, Handbook of Speech-Language Pathology, pg 1018).*

Medical necessity takes into consideration whether the service is essential and appropriate to the diagnosis and/or treatment of an illness, injury, or disease. Speech-language treatment provides the same benefits to individuals with autism as medication or medical procedures provide to individuals afflicted with other similar physical or bioneurological disorders, which are typically covered by health plans. Speech-language pathology services are "essential and appropriate" in treating Adam's speech and language disorder and are recognized as health care services by the Centers for Medicare and Medicaid Services of the U.S. Department of Health and Human Services.

Autism is treatable, with speech-language pathology services used to improve communication. The American Speech-Language-Hearing Association's (ASHA) *Treatment Efficacy Summary on Child Language Disorders* reports that children with language disorders benefit from treatment provided by speech-language pathologists as documented by clinical evidence (treatment efficacy summary attached). Language disorders described in the report are consistent with language problems associated with autism. Over 200 studies support the effectiveness of language intervention for an overwhelming majority of participants. Early intervention has been shown to be especially effective in treating young children with autism, as reported by Jane Garland, MD, Associate Professor, Department of Psychiatry at the University of British Columbia. She reports that "effective early intervention could make the difference between a life of dependency and a developmentally capable child."

Please reconsider coverage of speech-language pathology services for Adam. The services are medically necessary to treat his speech and language problems associated with autism, and studies show the treatment to be effective.

Sincerely,

_____ MA, CCC-SLP

Source: American Speech-Language-Hearing Association. (2002). *Appealing Health Plan Denials*. Rockville, MD.

APPENDICES

Appendix G

Appeal of Denied Claim

Sample Letter

Date

XYZ Health Plan
500 Main Street, Suite 101
Washington, DC 20011

> Re: Amy Lou
> Member ID#: 321654789
> Group Name: VWXY Group ID# 2500

Dear Claims Department:

I am responding to your letter of _____ (enclosed) denying speech-language pathology benefits for Amy Lou, specifically services to treat dysphagia (swallowing problems). Your letter states, "In this case, speech therapy is not a treatment that is commonly and customarily recognized throughout the doctor's profession as appropriate in the treatment of the diagnosed condition."   XYZ Health Plan should be aware that dysphagia evaluation and treatment is within the American Speech-Language-Hearing Association's (ASHA) scope of practice for speech-language pathologists. ASHA is the scientific, professional, and credentialing association for over 110,000 speech-language pathologists, audiologists, and speech, language, and hearing scientists.

Speech-language pathology and audiology services, and specifically, swallowing evaluation and treatment (deglutition) are recognized by the Health Insurance Association of American (HIAA) as important rehabilitation and habilitation programs. Speech-language pathology and audiology services are recognized as health services by the U.S. Department of Health and Human Services (DHHS) as well. These services are also specified in the accreditation manuals of the Joint Commission on Accreditation of Healthcare Organizations (JCAHO).

Forty-seven states require licensure for audiologists and forty-five states require licensure for speech-language pathologists. As you know, licensure signifies that a particular professional group is designated as the appropriate personnel to render a given set of services. I have enclosed a section from the *Medicare Program Integrity Manual*, "Special Instructions for Medical Review of Dysphagia Claims."

These instructions, which acknowledge the role of speech-language pathologists in the treatment of dysphagia, will help you to update your policy regarding treatment of swallowing disorders.

Enclosed you will also find additional information about dysphagia that will help you to understand better this health problem and its treatment. An XYZ representative indicated that Ms. Lou's age, 62 years, was a factor considered when reviewing this claim. I sincerely hope that swallowing treatment is viewed by XYZ as reasonable care for the elderly. Please reconsider the claim for speech-language pathology and dysphagia treatment submitted and make payment for the full amount requested.

Sincerely,

_____ MA, CCC-SLP

Source: American Speech-Language-Hearing Association. (2002). *Appealing Health Plan Denials.* Rockville, MD.

Appendix H

Example of a Department-Specific Policy and Procedures

Policy

The staffing plan of the Speech Pathology Department was developed to ensure that available staff is fully utilized in providing services to our patients in periods of normal volume and in times of high inpatient census. When staffing is inadequate to meet the demands for services, the staffing plan allows for referral of outpatients to other facilities. The staffing plan also ensures that patients are provided service by speech pathologists that specialize in the area of concern.

Procedures

Staffing/Patient Ratios

Each Speech Pathologist I is expected to spend approximately 60% of worked time in direct patient contact time. In order to achieve that level of productivity, about 75% of the worked time must be scheduled in patient care to compensate for cancellations and no-shows. The rest of the time is spent in documentation, follow-up, phone calls, treatment planning, patient conferences, meetings, and program development.

Budgeting for Staff

During the yearly budget process, an analysis is made of current and projected volume in order to determine the appropriate staffing levels for all locations and programs. Additional FTEs are added to the budget when volumes are projected to increase or there are indications from the staff or patients that current staffing levels are inappropriate.

Specialists and Specialty Teams

Speech pathologists are often recruited into the Speech Pathology Department based on experience and their areas of expertise. Speech pathology staff members who treat certain populations often serve specialty teams or certain clinics. These assignments are based on training, experience, expertise, and demonstrated competencies. Some staff members develop specialty expertise through our mentoring program.

Scheduling (See Scheduling Policy for more information.)

Inpatients: Inpatients are always a priority and must be seen within 48 hours of the referral. Therefore, inpatients are always scheduled before outpatients. If therapy is required, that speech pathologist will continue to follow the patient as long as he/she remains in the hospital.

Outpatients: Patients are scheduled for treatment based on the diagnosis, priority status, and needs. Outpatients are usually placed on a waiting list, unless they are considered priority based on the policy. If the patient cannot be scheduled immediately, the family is given a list of other programs and private practices near their home from the Resources Database in Chart Links. If the parents prefer to receive services here, then the patient is placed on the waiting list and scheduled as soon as an opening becomes available.

Coverage During Absence or Leaves (Maternity, Medical, Personal, etc)

When a speech pathologist is absent on a short-term basis, outpatients on the caseload are canceled. Inpatients are covered by other staff members as assigned by the inpatient coordinator.

If a speech pathologist is on an extended absence, including a maternity leave, our floating speech pathologist will cover most of the caseload, and other staff members at that location will try to absorb some patients on their caseloads. A temporary speech pathologist may be hired when available and as needed. If necessary, the person going on leave will determine which patients can be discharged on a temporary or permanent basis.

Staff Shortage

The Director of the Speech Pathology Department works closely with the Vice President for Patient Services and the Vice President of Human Resources to analyze staff ratios, turnover, volume and available space for additional staff. A detailed plan of recruitment and retention, which may include interim staffing measures, can be developed to alleviate shortfall. Staff concerns regarding the levels of staffing are also considered in developing staffing plans. The staffing plan also allows for referral to other facilities if the need exists.

High Volume Periods

During times of high volume with inpatients, outpatient speech pathologists are asked to see inpatients during cancellation times in their own schedule. If necessary, outpatients are canceled to accommodate the inpatients.

Source: Speech Pathology Department, Cincinnati Children's Medical Center, Cincinnati, OH.

Appendix I

Example of a Staff Competency Assessment

Pediatric Specialty Area SLP AAC Team	Check Level			Veri-fied	Competency Evidenced By				
Competency	Basic	Intermed	Advanced	Date	Demon-stration	Educ/ Training	Peer Obs	Self Report	Other
Administers standardized tests of speech, language, and social/ pragmatic communicative abilities appropriate for age groups from preschool through teen age.	X								
Demonstrates the ability to make appropriate adjustments during testing to allow for physical limitations and to make observations related to the child's current ability to functionally communicate (e.g. natural gestures, eye gaze, facial expressions).		X							
Assesses and identifies parent concerns.	X								
Conducts collaborative assessments to determine positioning, device selection, switch or direct access methods, and other assistive technology needs.		X							
Uses research guided, evidence-based assessment and tx approaches.	X								
Understands the principles of family centered evaluation and tx.	X								
Understands state early intervention eligibility criteria.		X							
Documents findings and outcomes in a manner consistent with department and medical center guidelines.	X								

Pediatric Specialty Area SLP AAC Team	Check Level			Veri-fied	Competency Evidenced By				
Competency	Basic	Intermed	Advanced	Date	Demon-stration	Educ/ Training	Peer Obs	Self Report	Other
Demonstrates a good understanding of the medical conditions associated with severe to profound verbal impairment or delayed language/speech development in children.	X								
Demonstrates the ability to conduct a comprehensive evaluation of communicative abilities (speech, language, social/pragmatic, abilities etc.).	X								
Establishes appropriate short and long term goals for both low and high tech communication devices.	X								
Uses learning and behavioral principles in tx.	X								
Sets age appropriate, functional and educationally relevant goals.	X								
Counsels and educates parents, staff, and teachers re: AAC.		X							
Demonstrates an understanding of the "total communication" approach to intervention and collaborates with other professionals involved AAC teams in a manner that is sensitive to the roles of other professionals in the evaluation and management processes.	X								
Knows how to obtain devices that are appropriate to needs of clients.			X						
Is familiar with and can program a range of low to high tech speech generating and non speech generating devices.			X						

Source: Pediatric Speech-Language Pathology Programs; Vanderbilt Bill Wilkerson Center, Department of Hearing and Speech Sciences.

Appendix J

A Look at Privacy and Confidentiality

The availability of information makes life easier in many ways. For example, with a simple Google search, we can now easily find information on even the most obscure topics. However, this abundance of information, or more specifically, the abundance of ways in which this information is gathered, stored, and potentially misused can be frightening.

Most of us know that we are not anonymous while surfing the Web. Through the use of "cookies" and other techniques, we leave a trail of where we have been. What we don't realize is how much information about us can be mined from seemingly innocuous everyday activities. For example, grocery store chains learn about your personal habits through the use of shoppers cards; electronic toll cards can access information about your travel habits, and soon, most cellular carriers will be able to pinpoint your exact location (for purposes of 911 emergency calls). Most of this information is collected incidentally, but the fact that it is out there is enough to make you wonder about your personal privacy. We have the right to a reasonable expectation of privacy when it comes to this personal, albeit inconsequential, data, but how are they really being used?

As professionals, we have access to sensitive information about our clients, and we have always had a duty of silence called confidentiality. This rule of ethics (ASHA, 2003) also has the weight of law behind it. At this point, everyone is familiar with the Health Information Portability and Accountability Act (HIPAA) and the privacy rule, but imagine how you would feel if sensitive information about your health, or the health of a loved one, were treated loosely by someone entrusted with that information. Then think of the way you handle the personal and protected information of those who have entrusted it to you.

HIPAA was actually designed to make the legal sharing of information among providers easier, not harder. To capture the spirit of this law, we must keep protected information private in an age when there are ever increasing ways to gather, store, and transmit it. Each clinician has a role to play. Everyone has the ability to ensure privacy of client information through everyday actions. Make a conscious choice to protect the privacy of information you have access to, and you will meet your moral, ethical, and legal obligations to those who trust you.

American Speech-Language-Hearing Association. (2003). Code of ethics (rev.). *ASHA Supplement 23*, 13-15.

Appendix K

Tips for Searching the Internet for Resources

Use these tips when searching the Web with your favorite search engine (e.g., Google, Yahoo). They can help you target your search and increase the number of relevant matches for your topic.

Be specific. If you are searching for a piece of software to help you manage your practice, don't simply type in "software," because you will get thousands of irrelevant possibilities. Instead, tell the search engine exactly what you want (i.e., **speech-language pathology practice management tools or software**). Likewise, if you are searching for a utility to clean a virus, be specific in what you ask for (e.g., **how do I remove code red visors from my Windows XP machine**?).

Use symbols to narrow your search. When searching for something, use the + sign to specify your parameters. For example, if you are looking for a way to get rid of a **virus**, don't type virus as you will get an overwhelming number of returns, including those for biological viruses. Instead, type **+remove + code red +Windows XP**. This will return only pages that have information on removing the code red virus from a Windows XP machine.

The – symbol works the same as the + symbol, except that it will only return pages that don't include the term after the - sign.

Use quotation marks. If you enter a series of words (as above), you will likely get a few targeted returns and an abundance of irrelevant returns because the search engine looks for each word in your query. To minimize this, enter the word or phrase you are looking for in quotations, and the engine will return only those pages that contain those words in that order. For example, entering telepractice may return too many possibilities. Entering **"telepractice in speech-language pathology"** will return pages with that exact phrase. Likewise, if you were searching for a free spam blocker, you could type **"free anti-spam download."**

APPENDICES

Appendix L

Speech-Language Pathologist Job Description

Position **Pay Grade:** **EEO-1 Category:** **FLSA Status:** __Exempt __Non-Ex.

Job Description

For HR Use Only

Code: XXXX-XX

Job Title: Staff Speech-Language Pathologist (SLP)

Corporation: Rehabilitation, Inc.

Department: Rehabilitation Services

Supervisor's Title: Supervisor of Speech-Language Pathology

Job Summary:

Under the general direction of the director or supervisor, the Speech-Language Pathologist functions with limited supervision and is responsible for evaluation and treatment of patients; documentation and communication of evaluation and treatment results; appropriate use of patient and professional related materials; presentations to staff, and program development, as assigned.

Job Qualifications:

Education: Master's degree in speech-language pathology from an accredited university.

Experience: Eligibility for Clinical Fellowship is required. One year of prior experience is preferred.

Knowledge/Skills/Licensure/Certification:

1. Must possess state license and Certificate of Clinical Competence or be eligible for Clinical Fellowship.

2. Demonstrated knowledge of the principles and practices of speech-language pathology and the ability to apply them in treatment programs.

3. Demonstrated ability to produce clear and concise written and oral reports.

4. Demonstrated ability to maintain patient and facility confidentiality.

5. Has met competency standards for designated procedures and client populations.

Major Job Responsibilities:

• Evaluate and treat patients with speech, language, swallowing, and cognitive-communication disorders in individual and group formats.

• Follow departmental policies and procedures for completing all required scheduling, billing, and clinical documentation.

• Participate in treatment teams, patient and family meetings, and departmental meetings.

• Provide in-service training for other disciplines.

• Participate in program development activities for clinical unit and SLP department.

Scope of Supervisory Responsibilities (if applicable):

☐ Department ☐ Multiple Depts. ☐ Facility ☐ Multiple Facilities

☐ Not Applicable

Customers: Routine contacts include patients, caregivers, visitors, physicians, hospital management and staff, employers, referral sources, insurance personnel, students, and student supervisors.

Age Specific Category: (Check all that apply)

☐ Infants ☐ Children ☐ Adults

OSHA Category: Hazardous Materials: ☐ Yes ☐ No

Bloodborne Pathogens: ☐ Type I ☐ Type II ☐ Type III

Approval Signatures: _____

Appendix M

Sample Performance Appraisal

Employee Name: _____ **Date of Appraisal:** _____

Supervisor: _____ **Review Period:** _____

Rating Scale:

Emerging Competence   Competent   Significant Competence

1   **2**   **3**   **4**   **5**

Explanation of Ratings:

1. Performance achieved was below the expected competency level set for the employee.

2. Improvement is required to meet the expected levels of performance.

3. Performance was at the expected competency level.

4. Overall results and behaviors meet the high expectations of Interactive Therapy Group.

5. Results and behaviors significantly exceed competency level and represent top performance. Performance provides exceptional value to our clients and Interactive Therapy Group.

N.A. not applicable   N.O. not observed

Service Delivery: Evaluations – the following *service related* items are considered in this category: (*rate 1 – 5 for specific competencies*)

Competency	Rating	Comments
Communicates effectively and works as a team member		
Follows guidelines for timeliness, recordkeeping, and format for required evaluation paperwork		
Makes appropriate recommendations based on subjective and objective measures		
Accurately administers tests and interprets testing results		
Thoughtfully counsels patient and/or family and caregivers as necessary		
Demonstrates competence in evaluating clients with a variety of delays/disorders		
Effectively communicates and works with related agencies and community members		
Demonstrates flexibility in altering plans during an evaluation as necessary		
Establishes and maintains a rapport with clients/family members/caregivers		
Handles patient/family member/caregiver questions appropriately		
Formulates appropriate referrals for additional testing		
Maintains confidentiality of client records		
Formulates appropriate goals and objectives for clients		

Additional Comments:

Service Delivery: Treatment – the following *service related* items are considered in this category: (*rate 1 – 5 for specific competencies*)

Competency	Rating	Comments
Writes treatment notes that are descriptive, objective, follow required format, and are submitted in a timely manner		
Implements therapy plans effectively during sessions		
Utilizes therapy time effectively		
Communicates goals and strategies for carryover with patient/family/caregiver		
Adheres to universal precautions and safety precautions		
Demonstrates independence and critical thinking in formulating and implementing goals		
Is punctual and organized for sessions		
Is proactive in maintaining a caseload		
Keeps self current with professional practices through continuing education activities		
Maintains confidentiality of client records		

Additional Comments:

Interpersonal Skills – the following *interpersonal* related items are considered in this category: (*rate 1 – 5 for specific competencies*)

Competency	Rating	Comments
Utilizes problem solving strategies in collaboration with supervisor, co-workers and clients		
Responds positively to suggestions/directions and incorporates action plan		
Is easily accessible via phone or e-mail		
Follows mandatory guidelines according to Policies and Procedures Manual		
Fosters teamwork		
Generates new ideas or process improvements		
Works in accordance with the company's missions and goals		
Acts with vision and purpose		
Shows progress towards professional goals		
Independently makes informed decisions		
Takes initiative to learn consistently		
Promotes diversity by showing respect and appreciation for each co-worker and customer whatever the person's background, race, age, gender, disability, values, lifestyle, perspectives, or interests		
Is flexible and accepts change with a positive behavioral response		
Works with others positively to resolve conflicts		
Acts in a manner consistent with professional and ethical behavior		
Takes responsibility for quality of own work and contributes to the organizational commitment to continuous quality improvement		

Additional Comments:

Communication Effectiveness – the following *communication skills* are considered in this category: (*rate 1 – 5 for specific competencies*)

Competency	Rating	Comments
Checks and responds to e-mail daily		
Attends and participates in quarterly mandatory staff meetings		
Refers to PHI Portal on the Web site for references and information		
Uses message board to communicate with peers and to gain new information at least 4 times annually (once per quarter)		
Communicates with the Regional Supervisor on a monthly basis (or at the discretion of the supervisor). Communication can be via e-mail, phone or face to face contact to update on caseload, and ask questions.		
Provides weekly education and training to clients (family and staff) as evidenced by documentation included in the treatment note.		
Contacts stakeholders at a minimum quarterly to address current, new or ongoing issues, as evidenced by documentation in the treatment notes.		
Communicates with colleagues with shared cases at a minimum monthly and documents communication within the treatment notes. Regarding collaboration that is not case specific, communication is at a minimum to be quarterly		
Independently utilizes the home/regional office resources to access information.		

Competency	Rating	Comments
Completes billing paperwork in a timely fashion, postmarked by the first day of the month, and provided to the appropriate regional specialist.		
Submits clinical reports (i.e. progress reports, discharge summaries, etc.) to required recipients (i.e. service coordinators, super-visor, home office) within ITG time frames.		

Additional Comments:

Technological Competencies – the following *technical competencies* are considered in this category: (*rate 1 – 5 for specific competencies*)

Competency	Rating	Comments
Enters and synchronizes data through Web site or Palm accurately, within 24 hours of rendering services.		
Utilizes word processing programs accurately and consistently		
Effectively accesses and utilizes Web site, message board, and employee portals on a weekly basis		
Contacts IT department after troubleshooting when encountering technical difficulties with Web site and/or Palm		

Additional Comments:

Employee Self-Appraisal

Employee Name: _____ Date _____

This page is to be filled out by the *employee* prior to the performance appraisal meeting.

My accomplishments over the past year are:

_____

_____

_____

_____

_____

Progress on goals:

_____

_____

_____

_____

Next 12 Month Goals for myself (should be compatible with organizational objectives):

1. _____

2. _____

3. _____

4. _____

5. _____

6. _____

Source: Interactive Therapy Group

Resources

Books

Accounting, 6th edition by C. T. Horngren, W. T. Harrison & L. S. Bamber. 2005. Prentice Hall, Upper Saddle River, NJ.

Accounting Principles, 6th edition by J. J. Weygandt, D. E. Kieso & P. D. Kimmel. 2002. John Wiley and Sons, New York, NY.

Coercion: Why We Listen to What "They" Say by D. Rushkoff. 2000. Riverhead Books, New York, NY.

Dale Carnegie's Lifetime Plan for Success by D. Carnegie. 2004. Galahad Books, New York, NY.

Essential Managers: Learning to Lead by R. Heller. 1999. Dorling Kindersley Publishing, New York, NY.

Financial and Managerial Accounting, 7th edition by C.S. Warren, J.M. Reeve & P.E. Fess. 2002. Thomson/South-Western College, Mason, OH.

Friendly Persuasion: My Life as a Negotiator by R. Woolf. 1990. Putnam Publishing Group, New York, NY.

Getting to Yes: Negotiating Agreement Without Giving In, 2nd edition by R. Fisher, W. Ury & B. Patton. 1991. Penguin Books, New York, NY.

Good to Great: Why Some Companies Make the Leap...and Other Don't by J. Collins. 2001. Harper Business, New York, NY.

How to Argue and Win Every Time: At Home, at Work, in Court, Everywhere, Every Day by G. Spence. 1995. St. Martin's Press, New York, NY.

Leadership in Healthcare: Values at the Top by C.F. Dye. 2000. Health Administration Press, Chicago, IL.

Op-Eds: A Cost-Effective Strategy For Advocacy by D. Zeck. 2000. The Benton Foundation, Washington, D.C.

Operations Management for Competitive Advantage by R.B. Chase, F.R. Jacobs & N.J. Aquilano. 2001. McGraw-Hill/Irwin, New York, NY.

Personal Political Power by J. Blackwell. 1998. Issue Management Co., Reston,VA.

Successful Managers Handbook by S. Gebelein, L. Stevens, C. Skube, D. Lee, B. Davis & L. Hellervik. 2000. Personnel Decisions Inc., Minneapolis, MN.

Take Action! A Guide to Active Citizenship by M. Kielburger & C. Kielburger. 2002. John Wiley & Sons, Hoboken, NJ.

The American Political Dictionary, 11th edition by J. Plano. 2002. Thomson/Wadsworth Publishing, Belmont, CA.

The Citizen's Guide to Lobbying Congress by D. DeKieffer. 1997. Chicago Review Press, Chicago, IL.

Three Steps to Yes: The Gentle Art of Getting Your Way by G. Bedell. 2002. Three Rivers Press/Crown Publishing Group, New York, NY.

Total Quality Handbook by D. L. Goetsch & S. Davis. 2000. Prentice Hall, Upper Saddle River, NJ.

You Can Negotiate Anything by H. Cohen. 1982. Bantam, New York, NY.

Web sites

American Health Information Management Association
www.ahima.org
> Information on HIPAA

Association for Electronic Health Care Transactions
www.afehct.org
> Information on HIPAA

CARF: The Rehabilitation Accreditation Commission
www.carf.org
> Information on accreditation

Centers for Medicare and Medicaid Services, HHS
www.cms.gov
> Responsible for Medicare, Medicaid, and HIPAA

Community Health Accreditation Program
www.chapinc.org
> Information on accreditation

Health and Human Services
http://aspe.hhs.gov/admnsimp
> Implementation guides for HIPAA

Joint Commission on Accreditation of Healthcare Organizations (JCAHO)
www.jcaho.org
> Information on accreditation

National Committee for Quality Assurance
www.ncqa.org
> Information on accreditation

Practice Source
www.practicesource.net
> Provides services for processing claims

Small Business Administration
http://www.sbaonline.sba.gov/starting_business/legal/forms.html
> Forms of business ownership

Working Group for Electronic Data Interchange, Strategic National Implementation Process
http://www.wedi.org/public/articles/index%7E3.htm
> Information and resources on HIPAA

Resources Available From ASHA

Practice Policy Documents (available on ASHA Web site, Members Only link)

Audiologists providing clinical services via telepractice: Position statement. (2004).

Audiologists providing clinical services via telepractice: Technical report. (2004).

Knowledge and skills in business practices needed by speech-language pathologists in health care settings. (2003). *ASHA Supplement 23*, 87-92.

Knowledge and skills in business practices for speech-language pathologists who are managers and leaders in health care organizations. (2004). *ASHA Supplement 24*, pp. 146-151.

Speech-language pathologists providing clinical services via telepractice: Position statement. (2004).

Speech-language pathologists providing clinical services via telepractice: Technical report. (2004).

Books and Guides

Appealing Health Plan Denials

ASHA Desk Reference 2002

Curriculum Guide to Managed Care, 1996

Getting Your Services Covered: A Guide for Working with Insurance and Managed Care Plans, 2004

Get Your Services Covered: How to Negotiate with Private Health Plans, 2003

Guidelines for Referral to Speech-Language Pathology

Health Plan Coding and Claims Guide, 2004

Negotiating Health Care Contracts and Calculating Fees: A Guide for Speech-Language Pathologists and Audiologists, 2004

The Power of One: Self-Advocacy Training Module, 1998

Regulatory Advocacy at the State and Federal Level, 1998

Reimbursement Boot Camp, 2003

Skilled Therapy: Medicare Coverage Guidelines for the Continuum of Care (videotape and workbook)

State and Federal Public Policy Advocacy Modules, 1999

RESOURCES

Web site www.asha.org

ASHA's Web site is arranged by four categories:

- For ASHA Members Only
  Information about clinical, practice and management issues such as reimbursement, marketing, telepractice, surveys, and salary information. Access to ASHA publications and membership directory.

- About ASHA
  General information about ASHA, legislation and advocacy (including HIPAA information), ASHA Leader Online, ethics, journal abstracts, certification information, career center

- For Students
  Information on certification and the Praxis exam, employment settings, finding a job.

- For The Public
  Information on certification, advocacy and outreach, speech and hearing development, information packets.

Index

5312